AN ADAPTED CLASSIC

NASSAU LEARNING CENTER
EAC, INC.
382 MAIN STREET
PORT WASHINGTON, NY 11050

A Raisin in the Sun

Lorraine Hansberry

D1269652

GLOBE FEARON
Pearson Learning Group

The publishers would like to acknowledge that the use of this text was granted by the kind permission of Jewell Gresham Nemiroff and Random House, 1999. Reprinted by arrangement with Random House, Inc.

Grateful acknowledgment is also made to Alfred A. Knopf, Inc. for permission to reprint 11 lines from "Dream Deferred" ("Harlem") from COLLECTED POEMS by Langston Hughes. Copyright © 1994 by the Estate of Langston Hughes. Reprinted by permission of Alfred A. Knopf, Inc.

Adapter: Emily Hutchinson
Project Editor: Wendy R. Diskin
Senior Editor: Lynn Kloss
Production Editor: Travis Bailey
Marketing Manager: Lisa Sandick
Art Supervision: Sharon Ferguson
Electronic Page Production: Jennifer Pereira
Cover and Interior Illustrator: Laurie Harden

Copyright © 2000 by Globe Fearon, Inc.,   299 Jefferson Road, Parsippany, NJ 07054. All rights reserved. No part of this book may be reproduced or transmitted in any form or by any means, electrical or mechanical, including photocopying, recording, or by any information storage and retrieval system, without permission in writing from the publisher. For information regarding permission (s), write to Right and Permissions Department.

ISBN: 0-835-95542-7

Printed in the United States of America
    5 6 7 8 9 10 06 05 04

Globe
Fearon

Pearson Learning Group

1-800-321-3106
www.pearsonlearning.com

CONTENTS

About the Author iv

Adapter's Note................................. v

Historical Background vi

Preface viii

Cast of Characters ix

Excerpt from "Dream Deferred" x

Act I

Scene 1: Friday morning........................ 1

Scene 2: The following morning 25

Act II

Scene 1: Later the same day..................... 42

Scene 2: Friday night, a few weeks later.......... 57

Scene 3: Moving day, one week later 66

Act III

An hour later.................................. 80

Reviewing Your Reading 97

ABOUT THE AUTHOR

Like the characters in *A Raisin in the Sun*, Lorraine Hansberry (1930–1965) lived for a time in an apartment in Chicago's Southside. Her family, however, was not as poor as the Younger family, and their apartment was not as cramped. She was the fourth and last child in the family. Her father was regarded by his neighbors as having earned a "fortune," but that wasn't quite true. He was a successful businessman of the middle class, more successful than most of his neighbors. Because of this, Lorraine was known as a "rich" girl in the Southside. She tells a story about being sent to school in a white fur coat in the middle of the Depression. The other kids beat her up and poured ink on the coat. She says from that moment, she became a rebel, distrusting any of the symbols of wealth.

In 1939, her father became determined to fight segregation in Chicago. He spent a great deal of money and considerable time in a legal case that went to the Supreme Court. The issue at stake was whether the Hansberry family or any African American family would be allowed to live in a "white neighborhood." Mr. Hansberry and his NAACP attorneys "won" the Supreme Court decision. After the family moved to a "white neighborhood," she says that "howling mobs surrounded our house." One of the rocks thrown by the mob almost took the life of the then eight-year-old Lorraine.

In 1959, Lorraine Hansberry became the youngest American, the fifth woman, and the first African American playwright to win the New York Drama Critics' Circle Award for Best Play of the Year.

She was just twenty-nine years old, and the play was *A Raisin in the Sun.* The only other play of hers that was produced during her lifetime was *The Sign in Sidney Brustein's Window*, a play about failing human relationships. This play had 101 performances on Broadway, the last one closing just a few hours after the playwright died of cancer on January 12, 1965. She was only thirty-four years old. She never got to see a performance of her play *Les Blancs*, which is set in Africa and deals with the conflict between native Africans and colonizers.

After her death, excerpts of her work (plays, letters, journal entries, and speeches) were put together in a play called *To Be Young, Gifted and Black.* The title of the play came from a speech she gave shortly before she died, and the phrase has become part of our language.

ADAPTER'S NOTE

In preparing this edition of *A Raisin in the Sun*, we have kept as close as possible to Lorraine Hansberry's original words. We have changed some of the vocabulary. We have also shortened and simplified some scenes and lines. Some of the footnotes will make the language clearer. Other footnotes will provide more historical detail. None of the plot of the play has been left out.

As in the original version of the play, we have included 11 lines from the poem "Dream Deferred" ("Harlem") by Langston Hughes. Lorraine Hansberry derived the title of her play from this poem, which you can read on page x.

HISTORICAL BACKGROUND

The setting of *A Raisin in the Sun* is Chicago's Southside, sometime between 1945 and 1958. World War II had recently ended, and the economy in the United States was strong. Homes were being built all over America for the growing families of the men who had returned from the war. In general, however, white families and African American families lived in segregated communities.

This was before the civil rights movement that began in the 1960s, and outright prejudice often went unchallenged throughout the country. It was also before the concepts of African American beauty and identity began changing. In a sense, the play was ahead of its time in dealing with issues that became more recognized later. For example, very few black women wore their hair in the natural style that Beneatha reveals in Act II. The play can be seen as anticipating the civil rights and women's movements of the 1960s, and also the trend to recognize and appreciate the African heritage of African Americans.

In the movies and in other media, the portrayal of African Americans at the time was dehumanizing. They were seen either as criminal or simple-minded. In contrast, Lorraine Hansberry's play portrays African Americans as complex human beings with dreams, hopes, conflicts, weaknesses, and strengths. By giving each character in the Younger family both positive and negative traits, Lorraine Hansberry is able to portray differing viewpoints about controversial issues. For example, Walter expresses certain attitudes that can be seen as offensive. He suggests that Beneatha should forget about being a doctor and just be a nurse or "get married and be quiet." This and other outbursts by Walter provide opportunities for the other characters to argue with him.

Hansberry wanted to present a realistic picture of the Younger family as they struggled to attain what any family wants: dignity and a suitable place to live. The play is a down-to-earth portrayal of the everyday problems of an African American family. The popularity of the play is a clear indicator that Hansberry was successful in accomplishing her goal.

PREFACE

The first play by an African American woman to be produced on Broadway (1959), *A Raisin in the Sun* won the Drama Critics' Circle Award. *A Raisin in the Sun* was first presented by Phillip Rose and David Cogan at the Ethel Barrymore Theatre, New York City, March 11, 1959. In 1961, it was produced as a movie starring Sidney Poitier, Ruby Dee, Diana Sands, and Louis Gossett. Lorraine Hansberry won a special award at the Cannes Film Festival for her screenplay for the film. In the final version of the film, however, nearly a third of Hansberry's screenplay had been cut. In 1992, the original screenplay was published with all the cuts restored. Based on the complete version of the play, The American Playhouse presented a television version of the play in 1989. It starred Danny Glover as Walter Younger and is available on videocassette.

CAST OF CHARACTERS
(In order of appearance)

RUTH YOUNGER
>A woman of about 30, the wife of Walter Lee Younger and a domestic worker

TRAVIS YOUNGER
>The 10-year-old son of Ruth and Walter

WALTER LEE YOUNGER
>A man of about 35, a chauffeur

BENEATHA YOUNGER
>A woman in her twenties, the sister of Walter, studying to be a doctor

LENA YOUNGER OR MAMA
>A recent widow, the mother of Walter and Beneatha

JOSEPH ASAGAI
>A young man from Nigeria, a student, and a boyfriend of Beneatha

GEORGE MURCHISON
>A young college student from a wealthy Chicago family, a suitor of Beneatha

MRS. JOHNSON
>A neighbor of the Youngers

KARL LINDNER
>A middle-aged white man representing the Clybourne Park Improvement Association

BOBO
>An associate of Walter

MOVING MEN

What happens to a dream deferred?[1]
Does it dry up
Like a raisin in the sun?
Or fester like a sore—
And then run?
Does it stink like rotten meat
Or crust and sugar over—
Like a syrupy sweet?

Maybe it just sags
Like a heavy load.

Or *does it explode?*

Langston Hughes

---

1. **deferred**   put off until a future time: postponed; *and/or*
   submitted to the wishes, opinions, or decisions of another

Act I

Scene 1

The Younger living room would be comfortable if it were not so cluttered. The furniture is now old and worn out. Still, we can see that each piece was selected with care and love and even hope, and then arranged with taste and pride. That was a long time ago. Now the couch is covered with doilies, arranged to hide worn spots. And here and there a table or a chair has been moved to hide parts of the carpet. Everything has been polished, washed, sat on, used, and scrubbed too often.

A section of the room has been made into a small kitchen area. The single window for these "two" rooms is located in the kitchen area. The only natural light the family gets is that which fights its way through this little window.

At left, a door leads to a bedroom shared by **MAMA** *and her daughter,* **BENEATHA**. *At right is a second room, which is the bedroom for* **WALTER** *and his wife,* **RUTH**.

Time: Sometime between World War II and the present.

Place: Chicago's Southside.

At curtain's rise: It is morning and dark in the living room. **TRAVIS** *is asleep on the make-down bed[2] at center. An alarm clock sounds from the bedroom at right.* **RUTH** *enters from that room and closes the door behind her. She crosses sleepily toward the window. As she passes her sleeping son, she reaches down and shakes him a little. At the window she raises the shade and the morning light comes in feebly. She fills a pot with water and puts it on to boil. She calls to the boy, between yawns, in a slightly muffled voice.*

---

2. make-down bed a couch that can be made into a bed

RUTH *is about 30. We can see that she was a pretty girl. By now, disappointment has begun to hang in her face. She gives her son a good, final, rousing shake.*

RUTH: Come on now, boy, it's 7:30! (*Her son sits up at last, still sleepy.*) I say hurry up, Travis! You ain't the only person in the world who has got to use a bathroom! (*The child, a handsome little boy of 10 or 11, drags himself out of the bed. He almost blindly takes his towels and "today's clothes" from drawers and a closet. He goes out to the bathroom, which is in an outside hall and is shared by another family or families on the same floor. Ruth crosses to the bedroom door at right and opens it. She calls in to her husband.*) Walter Lee! It's after 7:30! Lemme see you do some waking up in there now! (*She waits.*) You better get up from there, man! It's after 7:30 I tell you. (*She waits again.*) All right, you just go ahead and lay there. Next thing you know, Travis will be finished and Mr. Johnson will be in there. You'll be late, too! (*She waits, at the end of her patience.*) Walter Lee—GET UP!

(*She wipes her face with a moist cloth, runs her fingers through her hair, and ties an apron around her housecoat. The bedroom door at right opens and her husband stands in the doorway in his pajamas. He is a lean, intense young man in his middle thirties.*)

WALTER: Is he out yet?

RUTH: What you mean *out*? He just got in!

WALTER (*wandering in, still half-asleep*): Well, why was you doing all that yelling if I can't even get in there yet? (*stopping and thinking*) Check coming today?

RUTH: They *said* Saturday and this is just Friday. I hope you ain't going to get up here first thing this morning and start talking to me 'bout no money 'cause I 'bout don't want to hear it.

WALTER: Something the matter with you this morning?

RUTH: I'm just sleepy. What kind of eggs you want?

WALTER: Not scrambled. (**RUTH** *starts to scramble eggs.*) Paper come? (**RUTH** *points to the paper. He starts reading it.*) Set off another bomb yesterday.

RUTH (*bored*): Did they?

WALTER (*looking up*): What's the matter with you?

RUTH: Ain't nothing the matter with me. And don't keep asking me that this morning.

WALTER: Ain't nobody bothering you. (*He continues to read the paper. Then he sighs and looks at his watch.*) Now what is that boy doing in that bathroom all this time? He just going to have to start getting up earlier. I can't be being late to work on account of him fooling around in there.

RUTH (*turning on him*): Oh, no! He ain't going to be getting up no earlier no such thing! It ain't his fault that he can't get to bed no earlier 'cause a bunch of crazy good-for-nothing clowns sit up running their mouths in what is supposed to be his bedroom after 10:00 at night.

WALTER: That's what you mad about, ain't it? What I talk about with my friends just couldn't be important in your mind, could it? (*He looks at his wife for a moment.*) You look young this morning, baby.

RUTH (*bored*): Yeah?

WALTER: Just for a second—stirring them eggs. Just for a second, you looked real young again. (*He reaches for her. She gets out of his way. Then, dryly*) It's gone now—you look like yourself again!

RUTH: Man, if you don't shut up and leave me alone.

WALTER: First thing a man ought to learn in life is not to make love to no colored woman first thing in the morning. You all some eeeevil people at 8:00 in the morning.

(**TRAVIS** *appears in the hall doorway, dressed and quite wide awake now. He signals for his father to get to the bathroom in a hurry.* **WALTER** *hurries out.*)

RUTH: Sit down and have your breakfast, Travis.

TRAVIS: Mama, this is Friday. (*gleefully*) Check coming tomorrow, huh?

RUTH: You get your mind off money and eat now.

TRAVIS (*eating*): This is the morning we supposed to bring the 50 cents to school.

RUTH: Well, I ain't got no 50 cents this morning.

TRAVIS: Teacher say we have to.

RUTH: I don't care what teacher say. I ain't got it. Eat your breakfast, Travis.

TRAVIS: You think Grandmama would have it?

RUTH: No! And I want you to stop asking your grandmother for money, you hear me?

TRAVIS: I don't ask her. She just gimme it sometimes!

RUTH: Travis Willard Younger—I got too much on me this morning to be—

TRAVIS: Could I go carry some groceries in front of the supermarket for a little while after school then?

RUTH: Just hush, I said. If you through eating, you can get over there and make your bed.

(*The boy goes to the bed and more or less folds the bedding into a heap. Then he angrily gets his books and cap.*)

TRAVIS (*sulking*): I'm gone.

RUTH (*looking up from the stove*): Come here. (*He crosses to her and she studies his head.*) Take this comb and fix this here head! (TRAVIS *puts down his books and crosses to the mirror.*) 'Bout to march out of here with that head looking just like chickens slept in it! And get your jacket, too. Looks chilly out today.

TRAVIS (*with his jacket*): I'm gone.

RUTH: Got carfare and milk money?

TRAVIS: Yes'm.

(*His mother watches after him as he goes to the door. When she speaks, her voice has become a very gentle tease.*)

RUTH (*mocking, as she thinks he would say it*): Oh, Mama makes me so mad sometimes. I wouldn't kiss that woman good-bye for nothing in this world this morning! (*The boy finally turns around and rolls his eyes at her. He knows the mood has changed. He does not, however, move toward her yet.*) Not for nothing in this world! (*She finally laughs aloud at him and holds out her arms. We see that it is a way between them, very old and practiced. He walks to her and allows her to hug him. She holds him back from her, looks at him, and runs her fingers over his face gently.*) Now—whose little old angry man are you?

TRAVIS: Aw, golly, Mama . . .

RUTH (*pushing him playfully toward the door*): Get on out of here or you going to be late.

TRAVIS: Mama, could I please go carry groceries?

WALTER (*coming back in*): What is it he wants to do?

RUTH: Carry groceries after school at the supermarket.

WALTER: Well, let him go . . .

TRAVIS: I have to—she won't gimme the 50 cents.

WALTER (*to his wife only*): Why not?

RUTH (*simply*): 'Cause we don't have it.

WALTER (*to RUTH only*): What you tell the boy things like that for? (*Reaching down into his pants with a rather important gesture.*) Here, son— (*He hands the boy the coin, but his eyes are directed at his wife's.*) In fact, here's another 50 cents. Buy yourself some fruit today—or something!

TRAVIS: Whoopee—

WALTER: You better get to school now, son.

TRAVIS (*at the door*): OK. Good-bye. (*He exits.*)

WALTER (*pointing at him, with pride*): That's my boy. (*RUTH looks at him in disgust.*) You know what I was thinking 'bout in the bathroom this morning?

RUTH: No.

WALTER (*sarcastically*): How come you always try to be so pleasant?

RUTH: What is there to be pleasant 'bout?

WALTER: You want to know what I was thinking 'bout in the bathroom or not?

RUTH: I know what you thinking 'bout.

WALTER (*ignoring her*): 'Bout what me and Willy Harris was talking about last night.

RUTH: Willy Harris is a good-for-nothing loudmouth.

WALTER: Anybody who talks to me has got to be a good-for-nothing loudmouth, ain't he? Charlie Atkins was just a "good-for-nothing loudmouth" too, wasn't he? When he wanted me to go in the dry-cleaning business with him. And now—he's making one hundred thousand a year. One hundred thousand dollars. You still call him a loudmouth!

RUTH (*bitterly*): Oh, Walter Lee . . . (*She folds her head on her arms over the table.*)

WALTER (*rising and coming to her and standing over her*): You tired, ain't you. Tired of everything. Me, the boy, the way we live—this beat-up hole—everything. Ain't you? (*She doesn't look up, doesn't answer.*) So tired—moaning and groaning all the time, but you wouldn't do nothing to help, would you? You couldn't be on my side that long for nothing, could you?

RUTH: Walter, please leave me alone.

WALTER: A man needs for a woman to back him up . . .

RUTH: Walter—

WALTER: Mama would listen to you. You know she listen to you more than she do to me and Bennie. She thinks more of you. All you have to do is just sit down with her when you drinking your coffee one morning and

talking 'bout things like you do. Then you say easy like
that you been thinking 'bout that deal Walter Lee is so
interested in. Then you sip some more coffee, like what
you saying ain't really that important to you. The next
thing you know, she be listening good and asking you
questions and when I come back, I can tell her the
details. This ain't no fly-by-night deal, baby. I mean
we figured it out, me and Willy and Bobo.

RUTH (*with a frown*): Bobo?

WALTER: Yeah. You see, this little liquor store we got in
mind cost 75,000 dollars. The down payment would
be 'bout 30,000 dollars. That be 10,000 dollars each.
'Course, there's a couple of hundred to pay so's you
don't spend your life waiting for them clowns to
approve your license—

RUTH: You mean graft?[3]

WALTER: Don't call it that. See there, that just goes to
show you what women understand about the world.
Baby, don't nothing happen for you in this world 'less
you pay somebody off!

RUTH: Walter, eat your eggs, they gonna be cold.

WALTER: That's it. There you are. Man says to his woman:
I got me a dream. His woman say: Eat your eggs.
(*sadly, but gaining in power*) Man say: I got to take
hold of this here world, baby! And a woman will say:
Eat your eggs and go to work. (*passionately now*)
Man say: I got to change my life, I'm choking to
death, baby! And his woman say—(*in utter anguish
as he brings his fist down on his thighs*)—Your eggs
is getting cold!

---

3. graft   money used to get an unfair or illegal advantage

RUTH (*softly*): Walter, that ain't none of our money.

WALTER (*not listening or even looking at her*): This morning, I was lookin' in the mirror and thinking about it . . . I'm 35 years old. I been married 11 years and I got a boy who sleeps in the living room. (*very, very quietly*) All I got to give him is stories about how rich white people live . . .

RUTH: Eat your eggs, Walter.

WALTER (*slams the table and jumps up*): DAMN MY EGGS. DAMN ALL THE EGGS THAT EVER WAS!

RUTH: Then go to work.

WALTER: See—I'm trying to talk to you 'bout myself, and all you can say is eat them eggs and go to work.

RUTH: Honey, you never say nothing new. I listen to you every day, every night and every morning, and you never say nothing new. (*shrugging*) So you would rather be Mr. Arnold than be his chauffeur. So— I would rather live in Buckingham Palace.

WALTER: That is just what is wrong with the colored women in this world. They don't understand about building their men up and making 'em feel like they somebody. Like they can do something.

RUTH: There are colored men who do things.

WALTER: No thanks to the colored woman.

RUTH: Well, being a colored woman, I guess I can't help myself none.

(*She rises, sets up the ironing board, and starts sprinkling the clothes to prepare them for ironing.*)

WALTER: We one group of men tied to a race of women with small minds.

(*His sister* **BENEATHA** *enters. She is about 20, as slim and intense as her brother. Her thick hair stands wildly about her head, unruly from sleep. Her speech has a more educated feel than that of her family. She passes through the room and goes to the outside door, looking out to the bathroom. She sees that it has been lost to the* **JOHNSONS**. *She closes the door and sits down at the table.*)

BENEATHA: I am going to start timing those people.

WALTER: You should get up earlier.

BENEATHA: Really? Dawn, maybe? Where's the paper?

WALTER (*pushing the paper across the table to her*): You a horrible-looking chick at this hour.

BENEATHA (*dryly*): Good morning, everybody.

WALTER (*senselessly*): How is school coming?

BENEATHA (*in the same spirit*): Lovely, lovely. And you know, biology is the greatest. I dissected something that looked just like you yesterday.

WALTER: I just wondered if you made up your mind.

BENEATHA (*sharply*): And what did I answer yesterday morning—and the day before that?

RUTH: Don't be so mean, Bennie.

BENEATHA (*still to her brother*): And the day before that and the day before that!

WALTER: I'm interested in you. Something wrong with that? Ain't many girls who decide—

WALTER and **BENEATHA** (*together*): —"to be a doctor."
(*silence*)

WALTER: Have we figured out yet just exactly how much medical school is going to cost?

RUTH: Walter Lee, why don't you leave that girl alone and get out of here to work?

BENEATHA (*exits to the bathroom and bangs on the door*): Come on out of there, please! (*She comes back to the room.*)

WALTER: You know the check is coming tomorrow.

BENEATHA: That money belongs to Mama, Walter, and it's for her to decide how she wants to use it.

WALTER: Now ain't that just fine! You just got your mother's interest at heart, ain't you, girl? You such a nice girl—but if Mama got that money she can always take a few thousand and help you through school too—can't she?

BENEATHA: I have never asked anyone around here to do anything for me!

WALTER: No! And the line between asking and just accepting is big and wide—ain't it?

BENEATHA (*with fury*): What do you want from me—that I quit school or just drop dead? Which?

WALTER: I don't want nothing but for you to stop acting superior 'round here. Me and Ruth done made some sacrifices for you. Why can't you do something for the family?

RUTH: Walter, don't be dragging me in it.

WALTER: You are in it. Don't you get up and go to work in somebody's kitchen for the last three years to help put clothes on her back?

RUTH: Oh, Walter, that's not fair.

WALTER: Who said you had to be a doctor? If you so crazy 'bout helping sick people—then go be a nurse like other women—or just get married and be quiet.

BENEATHA: Well, after three years, you finally got it said. Walter, leave me alone. It's Mama's money.

WALTER: *He was my father, too!*

BENEATHA: So what? He was mine, too—and Travis's grandfather—but the insurance money belongs to Mama. Picking on me is not going to make her give it to you to invest in any liquor stores.

WALTER: Nobody in this house is ever going to understand me.

BENEATHA: Because you're a nut.

WALTER: Who's a nut?

BENEATHA: You—you are a nut. Thee is mad, boy.

WALTER (*looking at his wife and his sister from the door, very sadly*): The world's most backward race of people, and that's a fact. (**WALTER** *slams out of the house.*)

RUTH: Bennie, why you always gotta be pickin' on your brother? Can't you be a little sweeter sometimes?

(*Door opens.* **WALTER** *walks in. He fumbles with his cap, starts to speak, clears his throat, looks everywhere but at* **RUTH.**)

WALTER (*finally to* RUTH): I need some money for carfare.

RUTH (*looks at him, then warms; teasing, but tenderly*): Fifty cents? (*She goes to her bag and gets money.*) Here—take a taxi!

(WALTER *exits.* MAMA *enters. She is in her early 60s, full-bodied and strong, a beautiful woman. She carries herself with great pride, dignity, and nobility. Her speech, on the other hand, is careless. She tends to slur everything.*)

MAMA: Who that slamming doors at this hour?

(*She goes to the window, opens it, and brings in a feeble little plant growing in a small pot on the windowsill. She feels the dirt and puts it back out.*)

RUTH: That was Walter. He and Bennie was at it again.

MAMA: My children and they tempers. Lord, if this little old plant don't get more sun than it's been getting it ain't never going to see spring again. (*She turns from the window and looks at* BENEATHA.) What was you and your brother fussing 'bout this morning?

BENEATHA: It's not important, Mama.

(*She gets up and goes to look out at the bathroom. It is apparently free, and she picks up her towels and rushes out.*)

MAMA: What was they fighting about?

RUTH: Now you know as well as I do.

MAMA (*shaking her head*): Brother still worrying hisself sick about that money?

RUTH: You know he is. It's just that he got his heart set on that store—

MAMA: You mean that liquor store that Willy Harris want him to invest in?

RUTH: Yes—

MAMA: We ain't no business people, Ruth. We just plain working folks.

RUTH: Ain't nobody business people till they go into business. Walter Lee says colored people ain't never going to start getting ahead till they start gambling on some different kinds of things in the world— investments and things.

MAMA: What done got into you, girl? Walter Lee done finally sold you on investing.

RUTH: No. Mama, something is happening between Walter and me. I don't know what it is, but he needs something—something I can't give him anymore. He needs this chance, Lena.

MAMA (*frowning*): But liquor, honey—

RUTH: Well, like Walter say—people going to always be drinking themselves some liquor.

MAMA: Well, whether they drinks it or not ain't none of my business. But whether I go into business selling it to 'em is. (*stopping suddenly and studying her daughter-in-law*) Ruth Younger, what's the matter with you? You look like you could fall over right there.

RUTH: I'm tired.

MAMA: Then you better stay home from work.

RUTH: I can't stay home. She'd be calling up the agency and screaming at them, "My girl didn't come in today—send me somebody!" Oh, she just have a fit.

MAMA: Well, let her have it. I'll just call her up and say you got the flu—

RUTH (*laughing*): Why the flu?

MAMA: 'Cause it sounds respectable to 'em. Something white people get, too. They know 'bout the flu. Otherwise they think you been cut up or something when you tell 'em you sick.

RUTH: I got to go in. We need the money.

MAMA: Child, we got a great big old check coming.

RUTH: Now that's your money. It ain't got nothing to do with me. We all feel like that—Walter and Bennie and me—even Travis.

MAMA (*thoughtfully*): Ten thousand dollars—

RUTH: Sure is wonderful.

MAMA: Ten thousand dollars.

RUTH: You know what you should do, Miss Lena? You should take yourself a trip somewhere. To Europe or South America or someplace—

MAMA (*throwing up her hands at the thought*): Oh, child!

RUTH: I'm serious. Just pack up and leave! Go on away and enjoy yourself some. Forget about the family and have yourself a ball for once in your life—

MAMA (*dryly*): You sound like I'm just about ready to die. Who'd go with me? What I look like wandering 'round Europe by myself?

RUTH: These here rich, white women do it all the time.

MAMA: Something always told me I wasn't no rich, white woman.

RUTH: Well, what are you going to do with it then?

MAMA: I ain't rightly decided. Some of it got to be put away for Beneatha and her schoolin'. Ain't nothing going to touch that part of it. Nothing. (*She waits several seconds, trying to decide whether to say this to* **RUTH**.) Been thinking that we maybe could meet the notes[4] on a little old two-story somewhere, with a yard where Travis could play in the summer. We could use part of the insurance for a down payment and everybody kind of pitch in. I could maybe take on a little day work again, few days a week—

RUTH: Well, Lord knows, we've put enough rent into this here rat trap to pay for four houses by now . . .

MAMA (*looking around*): "Rat trap"—yes, that's all it is. (*smiling*) I remember just as well the day me and Big Walter moved in here. Hadn't been married but two weeks and wasn't planning on living here no more than a year. (*She shakes her head at the dissolved dream.*) We was going to set away, little by little, don't you know, and buy a little place out in Morgan Park. We had even picked out the house. (*chuckling a little*) Looks right dumpy today. But Lord, child, you should know all the dreams I had 'bout buying that house and fixing it up and making me a little garden in the back. (*She waits and stops smiling.*) And didn't none of it happen.

RUTH: Yes, life can be a barrel of disappointments, sometimes.

---

4. meet the notes make the payments on a loan

MAMA: Honey, Big Walter would come in here some nights back then and slump down on that couch. I'd know he was down then . . . really down. And then, Lord, when I lost that baby—little Claude—I almost thought I was going to lose Big Walter too. Oh, that man grieved hisself! He loved his children.

RUTH: Ain't nothin' can tear at you like losin' your baby.

MAMA: I guess that's why that man finally worked hisself to death. Like he was fighting his own war with this here world that took his baby from him.

RUTH: He sure was a fine man, all right.

MAMA: Crazy 'bout his children! God knows there was plenty wrong with Walter Younger—hard-headed, mean, kind of wild with women. But he sure loved his children. Always wanted them to have something—be something. That's where your husband gets all these notions, I reckon. Big Walter used to say, "Seem like God didn't see fit to give the black man nothing but dreams—but He did give us children to make them dreams seem worthwhile." (*She smiles.*) He could talk like that, don't you know.

RUTH: Yes, he sure could. He was a good man.

MAMA: Yes, a fine man—just couldn't never catch up with his dreams, that's all.

(**BENEATHA** *comes in, brushing her hair and looking up to the ceiling, where a vacuum cleaner has started up.*)

BENEATHA: What could be so dirty on that woman's rugs that she has to vacuum them every single day?

RUTH: I wish certain young women 'round here who I could name would take inspiration about certain rugs in a certain apartment I could also mention.

BENEATHA (*shrugging*): How much cleaning can a house need, for Christ's sakes.

MAMA (*not liking the Lord's name used thus*): Bennie!

RUTH: Just listen to her—just listen!

BENEATHA: Oh, God!

MAMA: If you use the Lord's name one more time—

BENEATHA (*a bit of a whine*): Oh, Mama—

RUTH: Fresh—just fresh as salt, this girl!

BENEATHA (*dryly*): Well, if the salt loses its savor—

MAMA: Now that will do. I just ain't going to have you 'round here reciting the scriptures in vain—hear me?

BENEATHA: How did I manage to get on everybody's wrong side by just walking into a room?

RUTH: If you weren't so fresh—

BENEATHA: Ruth, I'm 20 years old.

MAMA: What time you be home from school today?

BENEATHA: Kind of late. (*with enthusiasm*) Madeline is going to start my guitar lessons today.

(MAMA *and* RUTH *look up with the same expression.*)

MAMA: Your *what* kind of lessons?

BENEATHA: Guitar.

MAMA: How come you done taken it in your mind to learn to play the guitar?

BENEATHA: I just want to, that's all.

MAMA (*smiling*): Lord, child, don't you know what to do with yourself? How long it going to be before you get tired of this now—like you got tired of that little play-acting group you joined last year? (*looking at* RUTH) And what was it the year before that?

RUTH: The horseback-riding club for which she bought that 55 dollar riding habit that's been hanging in the closet ever since!

MAMA (*to* BENEATHA): Why you got to flit so from one thing to another, baby?

BENEATHA (*sharply*): I just want to learn to play the guitar. Is there anything wrong with that?

MAMA: Ain't nobody trying to stop you. I just wonders sometimes why you has to flit so from one thing to another all the time. You ain't never done nothing with all that camera equipment you brought home—

BENEATHA: I don't flit! I—I experiment with different forms of expression—

RUTH: Like riding a horse?

BENEATHA: People have to express themselves one way or another.

MAMA: What is it you want to express?

BENEATHA (*angrily*): Me! (MAMA *and* RUTH *look at each other and burst into loud laughter.*) Don't worry— I don't expect you to understand.

MAMA (*to change the subject*): Who you going out with tomorrow night?

BENEATHA (*with displeasure*): George Murchison again.

MAMA (*pleased*): Oh, you getting a little sweet on him?

RUTH: You ask me, this child ain't sweet on nobody but herself. (*under her breath*) Express herself! (*They laugh.*)

BENEATHA: Oh, I like George all right, Mama. But I could never be serious about him. He's so shallow.

RUTH: Shallow—what do you mean? He's *rich*!

MAMA: Hush, Ruth.

BENEATHA: I know he's rich. He knows he's rich, too.

RUTH: Well, what other qualities a man got to have to satisfy you, little girl?

BENEATHA: You wouldn't even begin to understand. George looks good—he's got a beautiful car and he takes me to nice places. He is probably the richest boy I will ever get to know and I even like him sometimes. But if the Youngers are sitting around waiting to see if Bennie is going to tie up the family with the Murchisons, they are wasting their time.

RUTH: You mean you wouldn't marry George Murchison if he asked you someday? That pretty, rich thing? Honey, I knew you was odd—

BENEATHA: No, I would not marry him if all I felt for him was what I feel now. Besides, George's family wouldn't really like it.

MAMA: Why not?

BENEATHA: Oh, Mama—the Murchisons are honest-to-God-real-*live*-rich colored people. The only people in the world who are more snobbish than rich white people are rich colored people. I thought everybody knew that. I've met Mrs. Murchison. She's a scene!

MAMA: You must not dislike people 'cause they well off, honey.

BENEATHA: Why not? It makes as much sense as disliking people 'cause they poor, and lots of people do that.

RUTH (*to* MAMA): Well, she'll get over some of this—

BENEATHA: Get over it? What are you talking about, Ruth? I'm going to be a doctor. I'm not worried about who I'm going to marry—if I ever get married.

MAMA and RUTH: *If!*

MAMA: Now, Bennie—

BENEATHA: Oh, I probably will. But first I'm going to be a doctor, and George, for one, still thinks that's pretty funny. I couldn't be bothered with that. Listen, I'm going to be a doctor and everybody around here better understand that!

MAMA (*kindly*): 'Course you going to be a doctor, honey, God willing.

BENEATHA (*dryly*): God hasn't got a thing to do with it.

MAMA: Beneatha—that just wasn't necessary.

BENEATHA: Well, neither is God. I get sick of hearing about God. What has He got to do with anything? Does He pay tuition?

MAMA: You 'bout to get your fresh little jaw slapped!

RUTH: That's just what she needs, all right!

BENEATHA: Why? Why can't I say what I want to around here, like everybody else?

MAMA: It don't sound nice for a young girl to say things like that. You wasn't brought up that way. Me and your father went to trouble to get you and Brother to church every Sunday.

BENEATHA: Mama, you don't understand. It's all a matter of ideas, and God is just one idea I don't accept. It's not important. I am not going out and be immoral or commit crimes because I don't believe in God. I don't even think about it. It's just that I get tired of Him getting credit for all the things the human race achieves through its own stubborn effort. There simply is no God—there is only man and it is *he* who makes miracles!

(MAMA *listens to this speech, studies her daughter, and rises slowly. She crosses to* BENEATHA *and slaps her powerfully across the face. After, there is only silence and the daughter drops her eyes from her mother's face.* MAMA *is very tall before her.*)

MAMA: Now—you say after me, in my mother's house there is still God. (BENEATHA *stares at the floor.* MAMA *repeats it.*) In my mother's house there is still God.

BENEATHA: In my mother's house there is still God.

MAMA (*walking away, then turning and looking back at* BENEATHA): Some ideas we ain't going to have in this house. Not long as I am the head of this family.

BENEATHA: Yes, ma'am.

(MAMA *walks out of the room.*)

RUTH (*almost gently*): You think you a woman, Bennie— but you still a little girl. What you did was childish— so you got treated like a child.

BENEATHA: I see. (*quietly*) I also see that everybody thinks it's all right for Mama to be a tyrant. But all the tyranny in the world will never put a God in the heavens!

(*She picks up her books and goes out. There is a pause.*)

RUTH (*at MAMA's door*): She said she was sorry.

MAMA (*coming out, going to her plant*): They frightens me, Ruth. My children.

RUTH: You got good children, Lena. They just a little off sometimes—but they're good.

MAMA: No—there's something come down between me and them that don't let us understand each other and I don't know what it is. One done almost lost his mind thinking 'bout money all the time. The other talks about things I can't seem to understand in no form or fashion. What is it that's changing, Ruth?

RUTH: Now, you taking it all too seriously. You just got strong-willed children, and it takes a strong-willed woman like you to keep 'em in hand.

MAMA (*sprinkling water on her plant*): They spirited all right, my children. Got to admit they got spirit—Bennie and Walter. Like this little old plant that ain't never had enough sunshine or nothing—and look at it . . .

(*She has her back to RUTH, who has had to stop ironing and lean against something and put the back of her hand to her forehead.*)

RUTH (*trying to keep* MAMA *from noticing*) You sure . . . loves that little old thing, don't you?

MAMA: Well, I always wanted me a garden like I used to see sometimes at the back of the houses down home. This plant is close as I ever got to having one. (*She looks out of the window as she replaces the plant.*) Lord, ain't nothing as dreary as the view from this window on a dreary day, is there? Why you ain't singing this morning, Ruth? Sing that "No Ways Tired." That song always lifts me up so. (*She turns at last to see that* RUTH *has slipped quietly to the floor, almost unconscious.*) Ruth! Ruth honey—what's the matter with you . . . Ruth!

Curtain

Scene 2

The following morning, a Saturday. Furniture has been moved and **MAMA** *is washing the kitchen walls.* **BENEATHA** *is spraying insecticide along the baseboards. The radio is playing rather exotic saxophone blues.* **TRAVIS** *is looking out the window.*

TRAVIS: Grandmama, that stuff Bennie is using smells awful. Can I go downstairs, please?

MAMA: Did you finish your chores?

TRAVIS: Yes'm—finished early.

(The phone rings. **BENEATHA** *answers it as* **WALTER** *enters from the bedroom.)*

BENEATHA: Hello? . . . Yes, he is. *(She tosses the phone to* **WALTER**.*)* It's Willy Harris again.

WALTER: Hello, Willy. Did you get the papers from the lawyer? . . . No, not yet. The mail doesn't get here till 10:30. . . . No, I'll come there. *(He hangs up and goes for his coat.)*

BENEATHA: Brother, where did Ruth go?

WALTER *(as he exits)*: How should I know!

TRAVIS: Aw, come on, Grandma. Can I go outside?

MAMA: Oh, I guess so. You stay in front of the house, though, and watch for the postman.

TRAVIS: Yes'm. *(He exits.)*

BENEATHA *(spraying under the sofa)*: There's just one way to get rid of these roaches, Mama! Set fire to this building! *(The phone rings.)*

BENEATHA (*at the phone*): Hello? . . . (*pause, and a moment of recognition*) Well—when did you get back? . . . And how was it? . . . Of course I missed you . . . Now? No . . . house cleaning. Mama hates it if I let people come over when the house is like this . . . You *have*? Well, that's different . . . Come on over. See you soon. *Arrivederci.*[5] (*She hangs up.*)

MAMA: Who is that you inviting over here with this house looking like this? You ain't got the pride you was born with!

BENEATHA: Asagai doesn't care how houses look, Mama—he's an intellectual.

MAMA: *Who?*

BENEATHA: Asagai—Joseph Asagai. He's an African boy I met on campus. He's been studying in Canada all summer.

MAMA: What's his name?

BENEATHA: Asagai, Joseph. Ah-sah-guy . . . He's from Nigeria.

MAMA: Oh, that's the little country that was founded by slaves way back . . .

BENEATHA: No, Mama—that's Liberia.

MAMA: I don't think I never met no African before.

BENEATHA: Well, please don't ask him a whole lot of ignorant questions about Africans. I mean, do they wear clothes and all that—

MAMA: Well, now, I guess if you think we so ignorant 'round here maybe you shouldn't bring your friends here—

---

5. *arrivederci* an Italian expression for "until we meet again"

BENEATHA: It's just that people ask such crazy things. All anyone seems to know about when it comes to Africa is Tarzan[6]—

(RUTH *comes in forlornly and pulls off her coat sadly. They both turn to look at her.*)

RUTH: Well, I guess from all the happy faces—everybody knows.

BENEATHA: You pregnant?

MAMA: Lord have mercy, I sure hope it's a little old girl. Travis ought to have a sister.

BENEATHA: How far along are you?

RUTH: Two months.

BENEATHA: Did you plan it, Ruth?

RUTH: Mind your own business.

BENEATHA: It is my business—where is he going to live, on the roof? (*There is silence following the remark as the three women react to the sense of it.*) Gee—I didn't mean that, Ruth, honest. I—I think it is wonderful.

RUTH (*dully*): Wonderful.

BENEATHA: Yes—really. (*There is a sudden commotion from the street. She goes to the window to look out.*) What on earth is going on out there? These kids—(*She throws open the window, and shouts of children rise up from the street. She sticks her head out to see better and calls out.*) TRAVIS! TRAVIS . . . WHAT ARE YOU DOING DOWN THERE? (*She sees.*) Oh Lord, they're chasing a rat! (RUTH *covers her face with her hands and turns away.*)

---

6. Tarzan a fictional character, the son of an English nobleman, abandoned in Africa as a baby

MAMA (*angrily*): Tell Travis to get himself up here, at once!

BENEATHA: TRAVIS . . . YOU COME UPSTAIRS . . . AT ONCE!

RUTH (*her face twisted*): Chasing a rat . . .

MAMA (*looking at* RUTH, *worried*): Doctor say everything going to be all right?

RUTH: Yes—she says everything will be fine . . .

MAMA (*immediately suspicious*): "She"—what doctor you went to?

(RUTH *just looks at* MAMA *meaningfully. She suddenly starts sobbing. The bell rings.*)

BENEATHA: Oh, my God—that must be Asagai.

MAMA (*to* RUTH): Come on now, honey. You need to lie down and rest awhile.

(*They exit.* BENEATHA *opens the door to a rather dramatic-looking young man with a large package.*)

ASAGAI: Hello, Alaiyo—

BENEATHA (*smiling*): Hello, Asagai. Please excuse everything. (*He smiles and comes in.*) I'm very glad you are back.

ASAGAI: Why? You were quite glad when I went away. What happened?

BENEATHA: You went away.

ASAGAI: Ahhhhhhhh.

BENEATHA: Before—you wanted to be so serious before it was time.

ASAGAI: How much time must there be before one knows what one feels?

BENEATHA (*to change the subject*): What did you bring me?

ASAGAI (*giving her the package*): Open it and see.

BENEATHA (*opening the package and drawing out some records and the colorful robes of a Nigerian woman*): Oh, Asagai! . . . You got them for me! . . . How beautiful . . . and the records, too!

(*She lifts out the robes and runs to the mirror with them and holds the drapery up in front of herself.*)

ASAGAI (*coming to her at the mirror*): You wear it well . . . very well . . . mutilated hair and all.

BENEATHA (*turning suddenly*): My hair—what's wrong with my hair?

ASAGAI: Were you born with it like that?

BENEATHA: No . . . of course not.

ASAGAI (*smiling*): How then?

BENEATHA: You know perfectly well how . . . as crinkly as yours . . . that's how.

ASAGAI: And it is ugly to you that way?

BENEATHA (*quickly*): Oh, no, not ugly . . . But it's so hard to manage when it's, well—raw.

ASAGAI: And so you mutilate it every week?

BENEATHA: It's not mutilation!

ASAGAI: I am only teasing you because you are so very serious about these things. Do you remember the first time you met me at school? You came up to me and you said: "Mr. Asagai, I want very much to talk with you. About Africa. You see, Mr. Asagai, I am looking for my *identity*!" (*He laughs.*)

BENEATHA (*sounding disturbed*): Yes.

ASAGAI (*still teasing, taking her face and turning it toward him*): Well, it is true that this is not so much a face of a Hollywood queen as a queen of the Nile. But what does it matter? Assimilationism[7] is so popular here.

BENEATHA (*sharply*): I am not an assimilationist!

ASAGAI (*his laughter fading*): Such a serious one. (*a pause*) So—you like the robes? They are from my sister's personal wardrobe.

BENEATHA (*with disbelief*): You—you sent all the way home—for me?

ASAGAI (*with charm*): For you—I would do much more . . . Well, that is why I came. I must go.

BENEATHA: Will you call me Monday?

ASAGAI: Yes. We have a lot to discuss. I mean identity and time and all that.

BENEATHA: Time?

ASAGAI: Yes. About how much time one needs to know what one feels.

BENEATHA: You see! You never understood that there is more than one kind of feeling between a man and a woman—or, at least, there should be.

---

7. **assimilationism** a policy of making different racial and cultural groups blend into the cultural traditions of another group

ASAGAI (*gently shaking his head*): No. Between a man and a woman there need be only one kind of feeling. I have that for you.

BENEATHA: I know—and by itself, it won't do. I can find that anywhere.

ASAGAI: For a woman it should be enough.

BENEATHA: I know—because that's what it says in all the novels that men write. But it isn't. I'm not interested in being someone's little episode in America—or one of them! (ASAGAI *has burst into laughter again.*) Oh, that's funny?

ASAGAI: It's just that every American girl I have known has said that to me. White—black—in this you are all the same. It's how I know that the world's most liberated women are not liberated at all. You all talk about it too much!

(MAMA *enters. She is immediately all social charm because of the presence of a guest.*)

BENEATHA: Oh, Mama, this is Mr. Asagai.

MAMA: How do you do?

ASAGAI (*total politeness to an elder*): How do you do, Mrs. Younger. Please forgive me for coming so early on a Saturday.

MAMA: Well, you are quite welcome. I just hope you understand that our house don't always look like this. You must come again. I would love to hear all about—(*not sure of the name of his country*)—your country. How many miles is it from here to where you come from?

ASAGAI: Many thousands.

MAMA (*looking at him as she would look at* **WALTER**): I bet you don't half look after yourself, being away from your mama. You better come 'round here from time to time to get yourself some decent home-cooked meals.

ASAGAI (*moved*): Thank you very much. Well, I must go. I will call you Monday, Alaiyo.

MAMA: What's that he call you?

ASAGAI: Oh—"Alaiyo." I hope you don't mind. It is what you would call a nickname, I think. It is a Yoruba word. I am a Yoruba.

MAMA (*looking at* **BENEATHA**): I—I thought he was from— (*She is uncertain.*)

ASAGAI (*understanding*): Nigeria is my country. Yoruba is my tribal origin.

BENEATHA: You didn't tell us what "Alaiyo" means. For all I know, you might be calling me Little Idiot or something.

ASAGAI: Well, I do not know just how to explain it. The sense of a thing can be so different when it changes languages. (*thinking*) It means . . . it means One for Whom Bread—Food—Is Not Enough. (*He looks at her.*) Is that all right?

BENEATHA (*understanding, softly*): Thank you.

MAMA: That's nice. Come see us again, Mr.—

ASAGAI: Ah-sah-guy . . .

MAMA: Yes. Do come again.

ASAGAI: Good-bye. (*He exits.*)

MAMA: Lord, that's a pretty thing just left! I guess I see why we are so interested in Africa 'round here.

BENEATHA: Oh, Mama!

(*She picks up the Nigerian dress and holds it up to herself in front of the mirror again. She sets the headdress on and then notices her hair again and clutches at it. She narrows her eyes as if trying to imagine something. Then suddenly, she gets her coat and gets ready to go out.*)

MAMA: Where you going?

BENEATHA: To become a queen of the Nile!

(*She exits. RUTH enters from the bedroom.*)

MAMA: Who told you to get up?

RUTH: Ain't nothing wrong with me to be lying in no bed for. Where did Bennie go?

MAMA: Far as I could tell—to Egypt! What time is it getting to?

RUTH: Ten-thirty. And the mailman going to come today just like he done every day for the last umpteen years.

(**TRAVIS** *enters suddenly with the mail.*)

MAMA (*her eyes wide*): It's really come?

RUTH (*excited*): Oh, Miss Lena!

(**TRAVIS** *goes to his grandmother with slow ceremony and puts the envelope into her hands. She accepts it, and then merely holds it and looks at it.*)

RUTH: Open it . . .

MAMA: Now don't act silly. We ain't never been no people to act silly 'bout money.

RUTH: We ain't never had none. OPEN IT!

(MAMA *makes a good strong tear. She pulls out the check and looks at it closely.* TRAVIS *and* RUTH *study it over* MAMA's *shoulders.*)

MAMA (*her face sobering into a mask of unhappiness*): Ten thousand dollars. (*She hands it to* RUTH.) Put it away somewhere, Ruth. Ten thousand dollars they give you. Ten thousand dollars.

TRAVIS (*to his mother*): What's the matter with Grandmama? Don't she want to be rich?

RUTH: You go on out and play now, baby. (TRAVIS *exits.* RUTH *turns to* MAMA.) You've gone and got yourself upset.

MAMA: If it wasn't for you all, I would just give that money away.

RUTH: Now what kind of talk is that? Mr. Younger would just be plain mad if he could hear you talking foolish like that.

MAMA (*stopping and staring off*): Yes, he sure would. We got enough to do with that money, all right. (*She stops then and looks firmly at her daughter-in-law.*) Where did you go today, girl?

RUTH: To the doctor.

MAMA: Now, Ruth, you know better than that. Old Doctor Jones is strange enough in his ways, but there ain't nothing 'bout him make somebody slip and call him "she" like you done this morning.

RUTH: That's what happened. I just slipped.

MAMA: You saw that woman, didn't you?

RUTH: What woman you talking about?

MAMA (*angrily*): That woman who—
(**WALTER** *enters in great excitement.*)

WALTER: Did it come?

MAMA: Can't you greet people before you start asking about money?

WALTER (*to* RUTH): Did it come? (**RUTH** *unfolds the check and lays it quietly before him.* **WALTER** *sits down and grasps it close and counts off the zeros.*) Ten thousand dollars. (*He suddenly pulls some papers out of his breast pocket.*) Mama, look. Old Willy Harris put everything on paper.

MAMA: Son, I think you ought to talk to you wife. I'll leave you alone if you want.

WALTER: I can talk to her later, Mama. Look—

MAMA: Son—

WALTER: WILL SOMEBODY PLEASE LISTEN TO ME TODAY!

MAMA: I don't allow no yellin' in this house, Walter Lee, and you know it. And there ain't going to be no investing in no liquor stores.

WALTER: But, Mama, you ain't even looked at it.

MAMA: I don't aim to have to speak on that again.
(*a long pause*)

WALTER: You ain't looked at it and you don't aim to have to speak on that again? You ain't even looked at it and you have decided—(*crumpling his papers*) Well, *you* tell that to my boy tonight when you put him to sleep on the living-room couch. (*turning to* **MAMA** *and speaking directly to her*) Yeah—and tell it to my wife, Mama, tomorrow, when she has to go out of here to look after somebody else's kids. And tell it to *me*, Mama, every time we need a new pair of curtains and I have to watch *you* go out and work in somebody's kitchen. Yeah, you tell me then! (**WALTER** *starts out.*)

RUTH: Where are you going?

WALTER: I'm going out!

RUTH: Where?

WALTER: Just out of this house somewhere—

RUTH (*getting her coat*): I'll come, too.

WALTER: I don't want you to come!

RUTH: I need to talk to you, Walter.

WALTER: That's too bad.

MAMA: Walter Lee—(*She waits and he finally turns and looks at her.*) Sit down.

WALTER: I'm a grown man, Mama.

MAMA: Ain't nobody said you wasn't grown. But you still in my house and my presence. And as long as you are, you'll talk to your wife civil. Now sit down.

RUTH (*suddenly*): Oh, let him go and drink himself to death! He makes me sick to my stomach! (*She flings her coat against him and exits to the bedroom.*)

WALTER (*throwing the coat after her*): And you turn mine, too, baby! (*The door slams behind her.*)

MAMA: Walter, what is the matter with you?

WALTER: Matter with me? Ain't nothing the matter with *me*!

MAMA: Yes, there is. Something eating you up like a crazy man. Something more than me not giving you this money. The past few years I been watching it happen to you. You get all nervous acting and kind of wild in the eyes—(**WALTER** *jumps up impatiently at her words.*) I said sit there now, I'm talking to you!

WALTER: Mama—I don't need no nagging today.

MAMA: Seems like you getting to a place where you always tied up in some knot about something. But if anybody ask you 'bout it you just yell at 'em and bust out the house and go out and drink somewhere. Walter Lee, people can't live with that. Ruth's a good, patient girl in her way, but you getting to be too much. Don't make the mistake of driving that girl from you.

WALTER: Why—what she do for me?

MAMA: She loves you.

WALTER: Mama, I'm going out. I want to go off somewhere and be by myself for a while.

MAMA: I'm sorry 'bout your liquor store, son. It just wasn't the thing for us to do. That's what I want to tell you about.

WALTER (*picking up the check*): Do you know what this money can do for us? (*puts it back*) Mama, I want so many things . . .

MAMA: Yes, son.

WALTER: I want so many things that it's driving me kind of crazy. Mama, look at me.

MAMA: I am. You a good-looking man. You got a job, a nice wife, a fine boy and—

WALTER: A job? I open and close car doors all day long. I drive a man around in his limousine and I say, "Yes, sir; no, sir; very good, sir." Mama, that ain't no kind of job. That ain't nothing at all. (*very quietly*) Mama, I don't know if I can make you understand.

MAMA: Understand what, baby?

WALTER (*quietly*): Sometimes it's like I can see the future stretched out in front of me, just as plain as day. The future, Mama. Hanging over there at the edge of my days. Just waiting for me—a big, looming blank space—full of *nothing*. Just waiting for *me*. But it don't have to be. (*pauses, kneeling beside her chair*) Mama, sometimes when I'm downtown and I pass them cool, quiet-looking restaurants where them white boys are sitting back and talking 'bout things . . . sitting there turning deals worth millions of dollars . . . sometimes I see guys don't look much older than me—

MAMA: Son, why you so interested in money?

WALTER: Because it is life, Mama!

MAMA: Oh. So now it's life. Money is life. Once upon a time freedom used to be life. Now it's money. I guess the world really do change.

WALTER: No—it was always money, Mama. We just didn't know about it.

MAMA: No, something has changed. (*She looks at him.*) You something new, son. In my time, we worried about not being lynched and getting to the North if we could and how to stay alive and still have a pinch of dignity, too.

Now here come you and Beneatha—talking 'bout things your daddy and me ain't never even thought about. You my children, but how different we done become.

WALTER: You just don't understand, Mama.

MAMA: Son, do you know your wife is expecting another baby? (**WALTER** *stands, stunned, and absorbs what his mother has said.*) That's what she wanted to talk to you about. (**WALTER** *sinks down into a chair.*) This ain't for me to be telling—but you ought to know. I think Ruth is thinking 'bout getting rid of that child.

WALTER: No, no. Ruth wouldn't do that.

MAMA: When the world gets ugly enough, a woman will do anything for her family. *The part that's already living.*

WALTER: You don't know Ruth, Mama, if you think she would do that.

(**RUTH** *opens the bedroom door and stands there a little limp.*)

RUTH: Yes, I would, Walter. (*pause*) I gave her a five-dollar down payment.

(*There is total silence as the man stares at his wife and the mother stares at her son.*)

MAMA (*presently*): Well, son, I'm waiting to hear you say something. (*She waits.*) I'm waiting to hear you say we a people who give children life, not who destroys them. (*She rises.*) I'm waiting to see you look like your daddy and say we done give up one baby to poverty and that we ain't going to give up another one. I'm waiting.

WALTER: Ruth—(*He can say nothing.*)

MAMA: If you a son of mine, tell her! (**WALTER** *picks up his keys and coat and walks out. She continues, bitterly.*) You . . . you are a disgrace to your father's memory. Somebody get me my hat!

Curtain

Act II

Scene 1

Time: Later the same day. **RUTH** *is ironing. She has the radio going.* **BENEATHA** *enters and* **RUTH'S** *mouth falls open.*

RUTH: What have we got on tonight!

BENEATHA (*wearing the costume* **ASAGAI** *brought*): You are looking at what a well-dressed Nigerian woman wears. (*She parades for* **RUTH**, *her hair hidden by the headdress.*) Isn't it beautiful? (*She walks to the radio and turns off the good loud blues that is playing.*) Enough of this assimilationist junk! (*She puts on a record. The music comes up, a lovely Nigerian melody.* **BENEATHA** *listens. She begins to dance.*)

RUTH: What kind of dance is that?

BENEATHA: A folk dance from Nigeria. It's a dance of welcome.

(**WALTER** *comes in during the performance. He has obviously been drinking. He watches his sister, at first with distaste. Then his eyes look off—"back to the past." He sees what we cannot, that he is a leader of his people, a great chief, a descendant of Chaka, and that the hour to march has come. He lifts both his fists to the roof, screaming.*)

WALTER: YEAH . . . AND ETHIOPIA STRETCH FORTH HER HANDS AGAIN!

RUTH (*dryly*): Yes, and Africa sure is claiming her own tonight. (*She gives them both up and starts ironing again.*)

WALTER (*in a drunken, dramatic shout*): Shut up! I'm digging them drums. Them drums move me! In my heart of hearts—(*He thumps his chest.*)—I am much warrior!

RUTH (*not even looking up*): In your heart of hearts, you are much drunkard.

WALTER (*shouting*): FLAMING SPEAR! (*He suddenly has an imaginary spear and is actively spearing enemies all over the room.*)

BENEATHA (*encouraging him*): OCOMOGOSIAY![8] FLAMING SPEAR!

WALTER: THE LION IS WAKING! (*He pulls his shirt open and leaps up on the table and gestures with his imaginary spear.*) Listen, my black brothers—do you hear the waters rushing against the shore?

BENEATHA: OCOMOGOSIAY! We do!

WALTER: Do you hear the beating of the wings of the birds flying low over the mountains?

BENEATHA: OCOMOGOSIAY! We do!

WALTER: Do you hear the singing of the women, singing to the babies in the great houses? (*The doorbell rings.*) OH, DO YOU HEAR, MY BLACK BROTHERS!

BENEATHA (*completely gone*): We hear you, Flaming Spear— (**RUTH** *shuts off the music and opens the door.* **GEORGE MURCHISON** *enters.*)

WALTER: Telling us to prepare for the GREATNESS OF THE TIME! (*He turns and sees* **GEORGE**.) Black Brother!

GEORGE: What are you talking about?

---

8. ocomogosiay with this shout, Beneatha links her voice to the Nigerian melody and identifies herself with her African heritage

RUTH (*embarrassed for the family*): Beneatha, you got company. What's the matter with you? Walter Lee Younger, get down off that table and stop acting like a fool . . .

(**WALTER** *comes down off the table suddenly and makes a quick exit to the bathroom.*)

RUTH: He's had a little to drink. I don't know what her excuse is.

GEORGE (*to* BENEATHA): Look, honey, we're going to the theater—we're not going to be *in* it. So go change, huh?

(**BENEATHA** *slowly lifts her hands and pulls off the headdress. Her hair is close-cropped and unstraightened.* **GEORGE** *freezes mid-sentence.* **RUTH's** *eyes all but fall out of her head.*)

GEORGE: What in the name of—

RUTH (*touching* BENEATHA's *hair*): Girl, you done lost your natural mind? Look at your head!

GEORGE: What have you done to your hair?

BENEATHA: Nothing—except cut it off.

RUTH: Now that's the truth. It's what ain't been done to it! You expect this boy to go out with you with your head all nappy like that?

BENEATHA (*looking at* GEORGE): That's up to George. If he's ashamed of his heritage—

GEORGE: Oh, don't be so proud of yourself, Bennie—just because you look eccentric.

BENEATHA: How can something that's natural be eccentric?

GEORGE: That's what being eccentric means—being natural. Get dressed.

BENEATHA: You're such an assimilationist, George!

RUTH: What does that mean?

GEORGE: Oh, it's just a college girl's way of calling people Uncle Toms.[9] But that isn't what it means at all.

RUTH: Well, what does it mean?

BENEATHA: It means someone who gives up his own culture and takes on the dominant, and in this case, *oppressive* culture!

GEORGE: Oh, dear, dear, dear! Here we go! A lecture on the African past! On our Great West African Heritage! In one second, we will hear all about the great Ashanti[10] empires. Then you'll talk about the great Songhai[11] civilizations, and the great sculpture of Bénin[12]—and then some poetry in the Bantu.[13] Then the whole lecture will end with the word *heritage*! (*nastily*) Let's face it, baby. Your heritage is nothing but a bunch of raggedy spirituals and some grass huts!

BENEATHA: GRASS HUTS! (RUTH *goes to her and pushes her toward the bedroom.*) You are talking about people who were the first to smelt iron on the face of

---

9. **Uncle Tom** a name for an African American who humbles him/herself to please and gain the approval of whites (from a character in *Uncle Tom's Cabin*, a novel by Harriet Beecher Stowe)
10. **Ashanti** a west African tribe
11. **Songhai** a great trading state of west Africa that flourished during the 15th and 16th centuries
12. **Bénin** a city in southern Nigeria famous for its "bronzes" (actually brass work), some of which dates from the 13th century
13. **Bantu** a group of African languages spoken generally south of a line from Cameroons to Kenya

the Earth! The Ashanti were performing surgery when the English were still tattooing themselves with blue dragons! (**RUTH** *pushes her through the bedroom door.*)

RUTH: Have a seat, George. (**GEORGE** *sits.*) What time is the show?

GEORGE: It's an 8:30 curtain. That's just Chicago, though. In New York, the standard curtain time is 8:40. (*He is rather proud of this knowledge.*)

RUTH: You get to New York a lot?

GEORGE: Few times a year.

RUTH: Oh, that's nice. I've never been to New York. (**WALTER** *enters.*)

WALTER: New York ain't got nothing Chicago ain't. Just a bunch of hustling people all squeezed up together— being "Eastern." (*He looks* **GEORGE** *over from head to toe. He notices his expensive clothing, include white buckskin shoes.*) Why all you college boys wear them stupid-looking white shoes?

RUTH: Walter Lee! (**GEORGE** *says nothing.*)

WALTER (*to* **RUTH**): Well, they look crazy—white shoes, cold as it is.

RUTH: It's the college *style,* Walter.

WALTER (*to* **GEORGE**): How's your old man making out? I understand you all going to buy that big hotel on the Drive? Shrewd move. Your old man is all right, man. I mean, he thinks *big,* you know what I mean? But I think he's kind of running out of ideas now. I'd like to talk to him. Listen, man, I got some plans that could turn this city upside down. I mean I think like he does. *Big.* Invest big, gamble big, even lose *big* if you have to, you know what I mean. It's hard to find a man on this whole Southside who understands my kind of thinking. (*He looks at* GEORGE *and leans in closely.*) Me and you ought to sit down and talk sometimes, man. Man, I got me some ideas . . .

GEORGE (*bored*): Yeah—sometimes we'll have to do that, Walter.

WALTER (*understanding the boredom, and offended*): Yeah—well, when you get the time, man. I know you a busy little boy.

RUTH: Walter, please—

WALTER (*bitterly, hurt*): I know ain't nothing in this world as busy as you colored college boys with your fraternity pins and white shoes . . .

RUTH (*covering her face with humiliation*): Oh, Walter Lee—

WALTER: I see you all the time, with the books tucked under your arms. And for what? What are you learning over there? Filling up your heads with sociology and psychology—but are they teaching you how to be a man? How to take over and run the world? They teaching you how to run a rubber plantation or a steel mill? No—just to talk proper and read books and wear them stupid-looking white shoes . . .

GEORGE (*looking at him with distaste*): You're all taken up with bitterness, man.

WALTER (*glaring at* **GEORGE**): And you—ain't you bitter, man? Ain't you just about had it yet? You got it made? Bitter? Man, I'm a volcano. Bitter? Here I am a giant—surrounded by ants! Ants who can't even understand what it is the giant is talking about.

RUTH (*suddenly*): Oh, Walter! Ain't you with nobody?

WALTER (*violently*): No! 'Cause ain't nobody with me! Not even my own mother!

RUTH: Walter, that's a terrible thing to say!

(**WALTER** *exits.* **BENEATHA** *enters. She is dressed for the evening in a cocktail dress and earrings, hair natural.*)

GEORGE: Well, hey, you look great! (*looking at her hair*) You know something? I like it. It's sharp. (*He helps her into her coat.*)

RUTH: Yes, I think so, too.

BENEATHA: See you later.

RUTH: Have a nice time.

GEORGE: Thanks. Good night.

(**RUTH** *continues ironing.* **WALTER** *comes back to the room.*)

RUTH: Walter—

WALTER (*yelling*): Don't start!

RUTH: Start what?

WALTER: Your nagging! Where was I? Who was I with? How much money did I spend?

RUTH: Walter Lee, why don't we just try to talk about it?

WALTER (*not listening*): I been out talking with people who understand me. People who care about the things I got on my mind.

RUTH: I guess that means people like Willy Harris.

WALTER: Yes, people like Willy Harris.

RUTH (*impatiently*): Why don't you all just hurry up and go into the banking business and stop talking about it!

WALTER: Why? You want to know why? 'Cause we all tied up in a race of people that don't know how to do nothing but moan, pray, and have babies!

(*The line is too bitter even for him. He sits down.*)

RUTH: Oh, Walter . . . (*softly*) Honey, why can't you stop fighting me?

WALTER (*without thinking*): Who's fighting you? Who even cares about you?

RUTH: Well—(*She waits a long time, and then she starts to put away her things.*) I guess I might as well go on to bed. (*more or less to herself*) I don't know where we lost it, but we have. (*then, to him*) I'm sorry about this new baby, Walter. I guess maybe I better go on and do what I started. I guess I just didn't realize how bad things was with us. (*She starts out to the bedroom and stops.*) You want some hot milk?

WALTER: Why hot milk?

RUTH: 'Cause after all you drank, you ought to have something hot in your stomach.

WALTER: I don't want no milk.

RUTH: You want some coffee then?

WALTER: No, I don't want no coffee. Why you always trying to give me something to eat?

RUTH (*standing and looking at him helplessly*): What else can I give you, Walter Lee Younger?

(*She stands and looks at him. Then she turns to go out again. He watches her going away from him. His mood is changing.*)

WALTER: It's been rough, ain't it, baby? (*She hears and stops, but she does not turn around. He continues talking.*) I guess between two people there ain't never as much understood as folks generally thinks there is. I mean like between me and you. (*She turns to face him.*) How we gets to the place where we scared to talk softness to each other. (*He waits, thinking.*) Why you think it got to be like that? Ruth, what is it gets into people who ought to be close?

RUTH: I don't know, honey. I think about it a lot.

WALTER: On account of you and me, you mean? The way things are with us. The way something done come down between us.

RUTH: There ain't so much between us, Walter. Not when you come to me and try to talk to me. Try to be with me . . . a little, even.

WALTER: Sometimes, sometimes . . . I don't even know how to try.

RUTH: Walter—

WALTER: Yes?

RUTH (*gently*): Honey, life don't have to be like this. I mean sometimes people can do things so that things are better. You remember how we used to talk when

Travis was born . . . about the way we were going
live . . . the kind of house. Well, it's all starting to
slip away from us.

(*He turns to her and they look at each other. Then they kiss,
tenderly. The door opens and* **MAMA** *enters.* **WALTER** *breaks
away and jumps up.*)

WALTER: Mama, where have you been?

MAMA: My, them steps is longer than they used to be.
Whew! (*She sits down and ignores him.*) How you
feeling this evening, Ruth?

(**RUTH** *shrugs. She is disturbed at having been
interrupted.*)

WALTER: Mama, where have you been all day?

MAMA (*still ignoring him*): Where's Travis?

RUTH: I let him go out earlier, and he ain't come back yet.
Boy, is he going to get it!

WALTER: Mama!

MAMA (*as if just hearing him*): Yes, son?

WALTER: Where did you go this afternoon?

MAMA: I went downtown to tend to some business.

WALTER: Where were you, Mama? You didn't go
do something with that insurance money,
something crazy?

(*The front door opens slowly, and* **TRAVIS** *peeks his head in.*)

TRAVIS (*to his mother*): Mama, I—

RUTH: "Mama, I" nothing! You're going to get it, boy!

TRAVIS: But I—

MAMA: Why don't you all never let the child explain hisself?

RUTH: Keep out of it now, Lena.

(MAMA *clamps her lips together.* RUTH *goes toward her son.*)

RUTH: A thousand times I have told you not to go off like that—

MAMA (*holding out her arms to her grandson*): Well, at least let me tell him something. I want him to be the first to hear. Come here, Travis. (*He obeys, gladly.*) Travis, you know that money we got in the mail this morning?

TRAVIS: Yes'm—

MAMA: Well, what you think your grandmama gone and done with that money?

TRAVIS: I don't know, Grandmama.

MAMA: She went out and she bought you a house! (WALTER *jumps up and turns away from all of them in a fury.* MAMA *continues, to* TRAVIS.) You glad about the house? It's going to be yours when you get to be a man.

TRAVIS: Yeah—I always wanted to live in a house.

MAMA: All right, gimme some sugar then. (TRAVIS *puts his arms around her neck. She watches* WALTER *over the boy's shoulder, and then, to* TRAVIS) Now when you say your prayers tonight, you thank God and your grandfather—'cause it was him who give you the house—in his way.

RUTH (*taking the boy from* MAMA *and pushing him toward the bedroom*): Now you get out of here and get ready for your punishment.

TRAVIS: Aw, Mama—

RUTH: Get on in there. (*She closes the door behind him and turns happily to her mother-in-law.*) So you went and did it!

MAMA (*looking at her son with pain*): Yes, I did.

RUTH (*raising both arms*): PRAISE GOD! (*looks at WALTER*) Please, honey, let me be glad. You be glad, too. (*She puts her hands on his shoulders, but he shakes himself free.*) Oh, Walter . . . a home, *a home.* (*She comes back to MAMA.*) Well, where is it? How big is it? When we moving?

MAMA (*smiling at her*): First of the month. It's a nice house, too. Three bedrooms, nice big one for you and Walter. Me and Beneatha still have to share our room, but Travis have one of his own. (*with difficulty*) I figure if the—new baby—is a boy, we could get a double-decker bed. And there's a small yard where I could maybe grow me a few flowers.

RUTH: Walter, honey, be glad.

MAMA: Now I don't want to make it sound fancier than it is. It's just a plain little old house. But it's made good and solid, and it will be *ours.*

RUTH: Where is it?

MAMA (*frightened at this telling*): Well, it's out there in Clybourne Park.

(**RUTH's** *joy fades quickly, and* **WALTER** *finally faces* **MAMA.**)

RUTH: Where?

MAMA: 406 Clybourne Street, Clybourne Park.

RUTH: Clybourne Park? Mama, there ain't no colored people living in Clybourne Park.

MAMA: Well, I guess there's going to be some now.

WALTER: So that's the peace and comfort you went out and bought for us today!

MAMA: Son, I just tried to find the nicest place for the least amount of money for my family.

RUTH: Wasn't there no other houses nowhere?

MAMA: Them houses they put up for colored in them areas way out seem to cost twice as much as other houses. I did the best I could.

RUTH (*her mood quickly changing*): Well, well! All I can say is—if this is my time in life—MY TIME—to say good-bye to these cracking walls!—(*She pounds the walls.*)—and these marching roaches!—(*She wipes at an imaginary army of marching roaches.*)—and this cramped little closet which ain't now or never was no kitchen! . . . then I say it loud and good, GOOD-BYE, MISERY! I DON'T NEVER WANT TO SEE YOUR UGLY FACE AGAIN! (*She laughs joyously.*) Lena?

MAMA: Yes, honey?

RUTH: Is there a whole lot of sunlight?

MAMA: Yes, child, there's a whole lot of sunlight.

RUTH (*going to the room where* TRAVIS *is*): Well, I guess I better see 'bout Travis. (*to* MAMA) Lord, I sure don't feel like punishing nobody today! (*She exits.*)

MAMA (*to* WALTER): Son, son, you understand what I done, don't you? I just seen my family falling apart today. We couldn't go on like we was today. When it gets like that in life, you just got to do something different.

(*She waits.*) I wish you say something, son. I wish you'd say how deep inside you, you think I done the right thing.

WALTER: What you need me to say you done right for? *You* the head of this family. You run our lives like you want to. It was your money and you did what you wanted with it. (*bitterly, to hurt her as much as he can*) So you butchered up a dream of mine—you—who always talking 'bout your children's dreams.

MAMA: Walter Lee—

(*He just closes the bedroom door behind him.* MAMA *sits alone, thinking heavily.*)

Curtain

Scene 2

Time: Friday night, a few weeks later. Packing crates fill the living room. BENEATHA *and* GEORGE *come in after a night out.*

GEORGE: OK, OK, whatever you say. (*They sit on the couch. He tries to kiss her. She moves away.*) Look, we've had a nice evening. Let's not spoil it, huh?

(*He again tries to kiss her. She turns away from him, not with distaste but with lack of interest. She is in a mood to keep on talking.*)

BENEATHA: I'm *trying* to talk to you.

GEORGE: We always talk.

BENEATHA: Yes, and I love to talk.

GEORGE: I know it, and I don't mind it sometimes. I want you to cut it out, see. The moody stuff, I mean. I don't like it. You're a nice-looking girl. That's all you need, honey. Forget the atmosphere. Drop the dramatic routine. It doesn't go with you. As for me, I want a nice, simple, sophisticated girl—not a poet, OK?

(*He starts to kiss her, she rebuffs him again, and he jumps up.*)

BENEATHA: Why are you angry, George?

GEORGE: Because this is stupid! I don't go out with you to discuss the nature of "quiet desperation" or to hear all about your thoughts. The world will go on as it is no matter what you think.

BENEATHA: Then why read? Why go to school?

GEORGE: Simple. You read to learn facts, to get grades, to pass the course, to get a degree. That's it—it has nothing to do with thoughts.

BENEATHA: I see. Good night, George.

(GEORGE *looks at her a little oddly, and starts to exit. He meets* MAMA *coming in.*)

GEORGE: Oh, hello, Mrs. Younger.

MAMA: Hello, George. How are you?

GEORGE: Fine, fine. How are you?

MAMA: Oh, a little tired. You all have a nice time?

GEORGE: Yes, a fine time. A fine time.

MAMA: Well, good night.

GEORGE: Good night. (*He exits.* MAMA *closes the door.*) Hello, honey. What you doing?

BENEATHA: I'm just sitting.

MAMA: Didn't you have a nice time?

BENEATHA: No.

MAMA: No? What's the matter?

BENEATHA: Mama, George is a fool—honest.

MAMA: Is he, baby?

BENEATHA: Yes.

MAMA: You sure?

BENEATHA: Yes.

MAMA: Well, I guess you better not waste your time with no fools.

BENEATHA: Thank you, Mama.

MAMA: For what?

BENEATHA: For understanding me this time.

(*She exits quickly and* MAMA *stands, smiling a little, looking at the place where* BENEATHA *just stood.* RUTH *enters.*)

RUTH: Now don't you fool with this packing, Lena.

MAMA: Oh, I just thought I'd sort a few things out.

(*Someone knocks on the door.* RUTH *opens it to admit the neighbor,* MRS. JOHNSON, *who has a newspaper under her arm.*)

MAMA: Hello, Mis' Johnson. Ruth, give Mis' Johnson some sweet potato pie and milk.

JOHNSON: Oh, honey, I can't stay hardly a minute. I just dropped in to see if there was anything I could do. (*accepting the food easily*) I guess y'all seen the news what's all over the colored paper this week.

MAMA: No, I didn't get mine yet this week.

JOHNSON: You mean you ain't read 'bout them colored people that was bombed out their place out there? (RUTH *takes the paper and reads it.*) Ain't it something how bad these here white folks is getting here in Chicago! Lord, getting so you think you right down in Mississippi. 'Course I think it's wonderful how our folks keeps on pushing out. You hear some of these Negroes 'round here talking 'bout how they don't go where they ain't wanted and all that. But not me, honey! (*This is a lie.*) Wilhemenia Othella Johnson goes anywhere, any time she likes. Yes I do!

MAMA: Don't you want some more pie?

JOHNSON: No thank you. This was lovely. I got to get on over home and have my midnight coffee. I hear some people say it don't let them sleep. But I finds I can't close my eyes right without that last cup of coffee.

MAMA: Ruth, give Mis' Johnson some coffee.

(RUTH *gives* MAMA *an unpleasant look for her kindness.*)

JOHNSON (*accepting the coffee*): Where's Walter tonight?

MAMA: He's lying down.

JOHNSON: Mmmmmm, he sure gets his beauty rest, don't he? Good-looking man. And soooo ambitious! I bet it was his idea y'all moving out to Clybourne Park. Lord, I bet this time next month y'all's names will have been in the papers plenty. (*holding up her hands to mark off each word of the headline she can see in front of her*) "NEGROES INVADE CLYBOURNE PARK—BOMBED!"

(MAMA *and* RUTH *look at the woman in amazement.*)

MAMA: We ain't exactly moving out there to get bombed.

JOHNSON: Oh, honey—you know I'm praying every day that don't nothing like that happen! But you have to think of life like it is.

MAMA: We done thought about all that, Mis' Johnson.

(BENEATHA *comes out of the bedroom in her robe and passes through to the bathroom.*)

JOHNSON: Hello there, Bennie! How's school?

BENEATHA (*coolly*): Fine, thank you. (*She goes out.*)

JOHNSON (*insulted*): Getting so she don't have much to say to nobody.

MAMA: The child was on her way to the bathroom.

JOHNSON: I know, but sometimes she act like she ain't got the time of day for nobody ain't been to college. 'Course I can understand how she must be proud and everything—being the only one in the family to make something of herself. I know just being a chauffeur ain't never satisfied Walter none. He shouldn't feel like that, though. Ain't nothing wrong with being a chauffeur.

MAMA: There's plenty wrong with it.

JOHNSON: What?

MAMA: My husband always said being any kind of a servant wasn't a fit thing for a man to have to be. He always said a man's hands was made to make things—not to drive nobody's car for 'em or (*looking at her own hands*) clean they houses. And my boy is just like him. He wasn't meant to wait on nobody.

JOHNSON: Mmmmm. The Youngers is too much for me! (*She looks around.*) You sure are one proud-acting bunch of colored folks. Well, I always thinks like Booker T. Washington[14] said that time: "Education has spoiled many a good plow hand."

MAMA: Is that what old Booker T. said?

JOHNSON: He sure did.

MAMA: Well, it sounds just like him. The fool.

JOHNSON: Well, he was one of our great men.

MAMA: Who said so?

JOHNSON: You know, me and you ain't never agreed about some things, Lena Younger. I guess I better be going.

---

14. Booker T. Washington an American educator (1856—1915) who founded Tuskegee Institute, a college in Alabama for African Americans

RUTH (*quickly*): Good night.

JOHNSON: Good night. You can keep the paper.

MAMA: Good night, Mis' Johnson.

(**MRS. JOHNSON** *exits.*)

RUTH: If ignorance was gold . . .

MAMA: Don't talk about folks behind their backs.

RUTH: You do.

MAMA: I'm old and corrupted. (**BENEATHA** *enters.*) You was rude to Mis' Johnson, Beneatha, and I don't like it at all.

BENEATHA: Mama, if there are two things we, as a people, have got to overcome, one is the Ku Klux Klan—and the other is Mrs. Johnson. (*She goes to her bedroom.*)

MAMA: Smart aleck. (*The phone rings.*)

RUTH: I'll get it.

MAMA: Lord, ain't this a popular place tonight.

RUTH (*at the phone*): Hello—just a minute. (*goes to door*) Walter, it's Mrs. Arnold. (*She waits and then goes back to the phone.*) Hello. Yes, this is his wife speaking. He's lying down now. Yes . . . well, he'll be in tomorrow. He's been very sick. Yes, I know we should have called, but we were so sure he'd be able to come in today. I'm very sorry. Yes . . . Thank you. (*She hangs up. **WALTER** enters.*) That was Mrs. Arnold.

WALTER: Was it?

RUTH: She said if you don't come in tomorrow that they are getting a new man. Walter, you ain't been to work for three days! Where you been? You're going to lose your job.

WALTER: That's right. Ain't it sad?

RUTH: Oh, Walter, with your mother working like a dog every day—

WALTER: That's sad, too. Everything is sad.

MAMA: What you been doing for three days, son?

WALTER: Well, Wednesday I borrowed Willy Harris's car and I went for a drive. Just me and myself, and I drove and drove. Then I drove back and I went to the Green Hat. And Thursday, I did the same thing. And today—today I didn't get the car. Today I just walked and walked. And then I went to the Green Hat. You all sad? And you know where I am going right now—

(**RUTH** *goes out quietly.*)

MAMA: I've helped do it to you, haven't I, son? Walter, I been wrong.

WALTER: No, you ain't never been wrong about nothing, Mama.

MAMA: Listen to me, now. I say I been wrong, son. That I been doing to you what the rest of the world been doing to you. Walter, I ain't never really wanted nothing that wasn't for you. There ain't nothing worth holding on to, money, dreams, nothing else—if it means it's going to destroy my boy. (*She takes an envelope out of her purse and puts it in front of him.*) I paid the man 3,500 dollars down on the house. That leaves 6,500 dollars. Monday morning I want you to take this money. Put 3,000 dollars in a savings account for Beneatha's medical schooling. The rest you put in a checking account—with your name on it. And from now on, you do what you want with it. It ain't much, but it's all I got in the world. I'm putting it in your hands. I'm telling you to be the head of this family from now on like you supposed to be.

WALTER: You trust me like that, Mama?

MAMA: I ain't never stop trusting you. Like I ain't never stop loving you.

(*She goes out, and* WALTER *sits looking at the money.* TRAVIS *enters, ready for bed.*)

WALTER: Son, I feel like talking to you tonight.

TRAVIS: About what?

WALTER: Oh, about a lot of things. About you and what you want to be when you grow up. In seven years you going to be seventeen years old. And things is going to be very different with us in seven years, Travis. One day when you are seventeen, I'll come home from my office downtown somewhere—

TRAVIS: You don't work in no office, Daddy.

WALTER: Not now. But after what you daddy gonna do tonight, there's going to be offices—a whole lot of offices.

TRAVIS: What you gonna do tonight, Daddy?

WALTER: I'm going to make a business deal that's going to change our lives. And one day when you 'bout seventeen years old, I'll go up to your room. You'll be sitting on the floor with the catalogues of all the great schools in America around you. And I'll say, all right, son, what have you decided? Just tell me where

you want to go to school and you'll go. Just tell me,
what is it you want to be, and you'll be it. Whatever
you want to be—yessir! You just name it, son, and I
hand you the world!

(**WALTER's** *voice has risen in pitch. On the last line, he lifts
Travis high.*)

Blackout

Scene 3

Time: Saturday, moving day, one week later. RUTH *is alone
in the living room, finishing the family's packing. She is
nailing crates and tying cartons.* BENEATHA *enters,
carrying a guitar case.*

RUTH: Hi, honey. (*pointing to a package*) Look in there and
see what I found on sale this morning. (RUTH *pulls
out some curtains.*) Look at that—hand-turned hems!

BENEATHA: How do you know the window size?

RUTH (*who hadn't thought of that*): Oh—well, they bound
to fit something in the whole house. Anyhow, they
was too good a bargain to pass up. You know what
I'm going to do soon as I get in that new house?

BENEATHA: What?

RUTH: Honey, I'm going to run me a tub of hot water. And
I'm going to get in it, and I am going to sit and sit
and sit in that hot water. The first person who knocks
to tell me to hurry up and come out—

BENEATHA: Gets shot at sunrise.

RUTH (*laughing happily*): You said it, sister! Hey, you know
what we did last night? Me and Walter Lee?

BENEATHA: What?

RUTH: We went to the movies. (*looking at* BENEATHA *to see if
she understands*) We went to the movies. You know the
last time me and Walter went to the movies together?

BENEATHA: No.

RUTH: Me neither. That's how long it been. But we went last night. The picture wasn't much good, but that didn't seem to matter. We went, and we held hands.

BENEATHA: Oh, Lord!

(*WALTER enters with a large, gift-wrapped package. He cannot hide his happiness. He is singing and snapping his fingers. He puts on some music, dances over to* RUTH, *and gets her to dance with him.*)

BENEATHA: Talk about old-fashioned Negroes!

WALTER (*stopping for a moment*): What kind of Negroes?

(*He says this in fun. He is not angry with her today, nor with anyone. He starts to dance with his wife again.*)

BENEATHA: Old-fashioned.

WALTER (*dancing with* RUTH): You know, when those New Negroes[15] have their convention, you are going to be the chairman of the Committee on Unending Agitation. (*He goes on dancing, then stops.*) Race, race, race! I can just see you someday, looking down on some poor cat on an operating table. Before you start the operation, you'll say, "By the way, what are your views on civil rights?"

(*He laughs again and continues dancing. The doorbell rings.*)

BENEATHA: Sticks and stones may break my bones, but words will never hurt me!

---

15. New Negroes The term the "New Negro" first appeared during the Harlem Renaissance of the 1920s. This era saw a burst of creativity in music, literature, and the arts by African Americans in the Harlem district of New York's Manhattan. African American writers and thinkers of the time talked about the New Negro. One newspaper said this: "The NEW NEGRO, unlike the old-time negro, does not fear the face of the day."

(**BENEATHA** *opens the door and is surprised to see a quiet-looking middle-aged white man in a business suit. He is holding his hat and a briefcase in his hand and looking at a small piece of paper.*)

MAN: Uh, how do you do, miss. I am looking for a Mrs.— (*He looks at the slip of paper*) Lena Younger?

BENEATHA: Oh, yes, that's my mother. Excuse me. (*She closes the door and turns to quiet the other two.*) Ruth! Brother! (*She mouths these words, not saying them out loud: "There's a white man at the door!" They stop dancing and turn off the music.* **BENEATHA** *opens the door.*) Uh, come in, please.

MAN (*coming in*): Thank you.

BENEATHA: My mother isn't here just now. Is it business?

MAN: Yes. Well, of a sort.

WALTER: Have a seat. I'm Mrs. Younger's son. I look after most of her business matters.

(**RUTH** *and* **BENEATHA** *exchange amused glances.*)

MAN (*sitting*): Well, my name is Karl Lindner . . .

WALTER (*stretching out his hand*): Walter Younger. This is my wife and my sister.

LINDNER: How do you do.

WALTER (*sitting down*): What can we do for you, Mr. Lindner?

LINDNER: Well, I represent the Clybourne Park Improvement Association. We have had it brought to our attention at the last meeting that you people— or at least your mother—has bought a house at 406 Clybourne Street.

WALTER: That's right. Care for something to drink?

LINDNER (*upset for some reason*): No, thank you.

RUTH: Some coffee?

LINDNER: Thank you, nothing at all.

(**BENEATHA** *is watching the man carefully.*)

LINDNER: Well, I don't know how much you folks know about our organization. It is one of these community groups set up to look after—oh, you know, things like block upkeep and special projects. We also have what we call our New Neighbors Welcoming Committee. I'm the chairman of the committee. We go around and see the new people who move into the neighborhood. We sort of give them the lowdown on the way we do things out in Clybourne Park.

BENEATHA (*understanding the two meanings, which escape* **RUTH** *and* **WALTER**): I see.

LINDNER: And we also have the category of what we call (*He looks elsewhere.*)—uh—special community problems . . .

BENEATHA: Yes—and what are some of those?

WALTER: Girl, let the man talk.

LINDNER: Thank you. I would like to explain this thing in my own way. I'm going to try to get right to the point. I'm sure we'll all appreciate that in the long run.

RUTH (*still not understanding*): Would you like another chair? You don't look comfortable.

LINDNER: No, thank you. Please. Well, I'll get right to the point. I am sure you people must know about some of the incidents that have happened in various parts

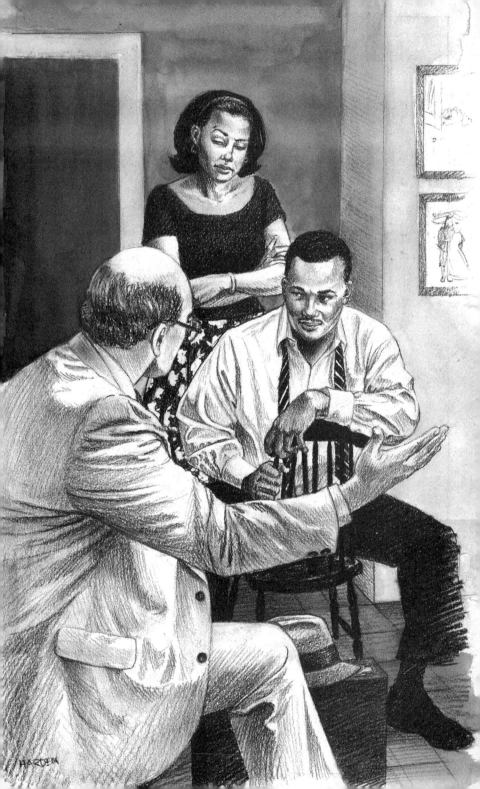

of the city when colored people have moved into certain areas. (**BENEATHA** *sighs and starts tossing a piece of fruit up and down in the air.*) Well, we are trying to prevent that sort of thing. We feel that most of the trouble in this world exists because people just don't sit down and talk to each other.

RUTH: You can say that again, mister.

LINDNER: Yes, that's the way we feel out in Clybourne Park. And that's why I was elected to come here this afternoon and talk to you people. Friendly-like, you know. The way people should talk and see if we can find some way to work this thing out. As I say, it's all about *caring* about the other fellow. Anybody can see that you are a nice family of folks, hard-working and honest, I'm sure. Today everybody knows what it means to be on the outside of *something*. And of course, there is always somebody who is out to take advantage of people who don't always understand.

WALTER: What do you mean?

LINDNER: Well, you see, our community is made up of people who've worked hard for years to build up that little community. They're not rich and fancy people. They're just hard-working, honest people who don't really have much but those little homes. Now, you've got to admit that a man has the right to want to have the neighborhood he lives in a certain kind of way. I want you to believe me when I tell you that race prejudice simply doesn't enter into it. It is a matter of the people of Clybourne Park believing, for the happiness of all concerned, that our Negro families are happier when they live in their own communities.

BENEATHA (*with a grand and bitter gesture*): This, friends, is the Welcoming Committee!

WALTER: Is this what you came marching all the way over here to tell us?

LINDNER: Well, now we've been having a fine conversation. I hope you'll hear me all the way through.

WALTER (*tightly*): Go ahead, man.

LINDNER: You see, we are prepared to make your family a very generous offer. We will buy the house from you for more than you paid for it.

WALTER: Are you through?

LINDNER: Well, I want to give you the exact terms of the financial arrangement.

WALTER: We don't want to hear no exact terms. I want to know if you got any more to tell us 'bout how people ought to sit down and talk to each other . . . Get out of my house, man.

(*He turns his back and walks to the door.*)

LINDNER: Well, I don't understand why you people are reacting this way. What do you think you are going to gain by moving to a place where you just aren't wanted? People can get awful worked up when they feel that their whole way of life and everything they've ever worked for is threatened.

WALTER: Get out!

LINDNER (*at the door, holding a small card*): Well, I'm sorry it went like this.

WALTER: Get out.

LINDNER (*almost sadly*): You just can't force people to change their hearts, son.

(*He turns and puts his card on a table and exits.* WALTER *slams the door.* RUTH *just sits and* BENEATHA *just stands. They say nothing.* MAMA *and* TRAVIS *enter.*)

MAMA: Well, this all the packing got done since I left this morning? What time the moving men due?

BENEATHA: Four o'clock. You had a caller, Mama.

MAMA: Sure enough—who?

BENEATHA: The Clybourne Park Welcoming Committee. They said they're sure going to be glad to see you when you get there.

WALTER: Yeah, they said they can't hardly wait to see your face. They said the one thing they don't have, that they just dying to have out there, is a fine family of fine colored people. (*to* RUTH *and* BENEATHA) Ain't that right!

Ruth: Yeah! He left his card.

BENEATHA (*handing card to* MAMA): In case.

(MAMA *reads it and throws it on the floor, understanding. She sits down.*)

MAMA: Father, give us strength. Did he threaten us?

BENEATHA: Oh, Mama, they don't do it like that any more. He talked Brotherhood. He said everybody ought to learn how to sit down and hate each other with good Christian fellowship.

(*She and* WALTER *shake hands to ridicule the remark.*)

MAMA (*sadly*): Lord, protect us . . .

RUTH: You should hear the money those folks raised to buy the house from us. All we paid and then some.

BENEATHA: What they think we going to do—eat 'em?

RUTH: No, honey, marry 'em.

(WALTER *comes to* MAMA *suddenly and squeezes her in his arms with all his strength. She is overwhelmed and delighted by it.* WALTER *then slips down on his knees beside her, his arms still around her.*)

WALTER: Mama, you know what it means to climb up in the chariot? What the old song say, Mama? "I got wings . . . you got wings . . . all God's children got wings. When I get to heaven, gonna put on my wings, gonna fly all over God's heaven . . ."

RUTH (*pointing to the gift-wrapped package*): Walter, now?

WALTER (*to* RUTH, *who is carrying the package across to them*): I don't know. Do you think she deserves it?

MAMA: What is that?

WALTER (*taking the box and putting it in front of* MAMA): Well, what you all think? Should we give it to her?

RUTH: Oh, she was pretty good today.

BENEATHA: Open it, Mama.

WALTER (*sweetly*): Open it, Mama. It's for you.

(MAMA *looks in his eyes. It is the first present in her life without it being Christmas. Slowly she opens her package and lifts out, one by one, a brand-new sparkling set of gardening tools.*)

TRAVIS: Daddy, can I give her mine now?

WALTER: All right, son. (TRAVIS *goes to get his gift.*)

MAMA: Now I don't have to use my knives and forks no more to garden.

WALTER: Travis didn't want to go in with the rest of us, Mama. He got his own. We don't know what it is.

TRAVIS (*racing back with a large hatbox*): Here!

MAMA: Lord have mercy, baby. You done gone and bought your grandmother a hat?

TRAVIS (*very proud*): Open it!

(*She does and lifts out a very elaborate, wide gardening hat.*)

MAMA: This is a beautiful hat. I always wanted one just like it. Bless your heart. This is the prettiest hat I ever owned.

(*The doorbell rings.*)

BENEATHA: That couldn't be the movers. It's not even 2:00 yet.

WALTER: I'll get it.

(*He goes to the door and throws it open. Standing there is a very slight, little man in a not-too-prosperous business suit. He has haunted, frightened eyes and a hat pulled down around his forehead. WALTER looks past the little man into the empty hallway.*)

WALTER: Where's Willy, man?

BOBO: He ain't with me.

WALTER: Oh, come on in. You know my wife.

BOBO: Yes. How are you, Miss Ruth?

RUTH: Hello, Bobo.

WALTER: You right on time today . . . right on time. That's the way! (*He slaps* **BOBO** *on his back.*) Sit down . . . let's hear.

BOBO (*his frightened eyes on the floor*): Could I please get a drink of water before I tell you about it, Walter Lee?

(**RUTH** *gets a glass of water for* **BOBO**.)

WALTER: There ain't nothing wrong, is there?

BOBO: Let me tell you, Walter Lee. I mean about the money I put in, Walter Lee . . .

WALTER: What about the money you put in?

BOBO: Well, it wasn't as much as we told you—me and Willy. (*He stops.*) I'm sorry, Walter. I got a real bad feeling about it.

WALTER: Man, what you telling me about all this for? Tell me what happened in Springfield.

RUTH: What was supposed to happen there?

BOBO (*to her*): This deal that me and Walter went into with Willy. Me and Willy was going to spread some money 'round so we wouldn't have to wait so long for the liquor license. Everybody said that was the way you had to do, you understand, Miss Ruth?

WALTER: Man—what happened down there?

BOBO (*near tears*): I'm trying to tell you, Walter.

WALTER (*screaming, suddenly*): THEN TELL ME!

BOBO: Man, I didn't go to Springfield yesterday. When I got to the train station at eight o'clock, like we planned . . . man, *Willy didn't never show up.*

WALTER: Why? Where was he? Where is he?

Bobo: That's what I'm trying to tell you. I don't know. I waited six hours. I called his house. And I waited in that station for six hours. (*breaking into tears*) That was all the extra money I had in the world. Man, *Willy is gone.*

Walter: Gone? What you mean Willy is gone? He's got to be somewhere. We just got to find him. Me and you got to find him. We got to!

Bobo: What's the matter with you, Walter? *When a cat take off with your money, he don't leave you no road maps!*

Walter: Oh, God, don't let it be true. THAT MONEY IS MADE OUT OF MY FATHER'S FLESH!

Bobo: I'm sorry, Walter. I had my life staked on this deal, too . . .

(*He exits.*)

Mama (*to* **Walter**): Son, son, is it gone? Son, I gave you 6,500 dollars. Is it gone? All of it? Beneatha's money, too?

Walter: Mama . . . I never went to the bank at all.

Mama (*not wanting to believe him*): You mean . . . your sister's school money . . . you used that, too? Walter?

Walter: Yes! All of it. It's all gone.

(*There is total silence.* **Ruth** *covers her face with her hands.* **Beneatha** *stands against a wall.* **Mama** *looks at her son and then, without thinking about it, starts to beat him in the face.* **Beneatha** *goes to them and stops it.*)

Beneatha: Mama!

(**MAMA** *stops and looks at both of her children. She rises slowly and wanders aimlessly away from them.*)

MAMA: I seen . . . him . . . your father night after night . . . come in. He'd look at that rug . . . and then look at me . . . the red showing in his eyes . . . the veins moving in his head. I seen him grow thin and old before he was forty. Working and working and working like somebody's old horse . . . killing himself . . . and you—you give it all away in a day. (*She raises her arms to strike him again.*)

BENEATHA: Mama—

MAMA: Oh, God. (*She looks up.*) Look down here—and show me the strength.

BENEATHA: Mama—

MAMA (*folding over*): Strength . . .

BENEATHA (*begging*): Mama . . .

MAMA: Strength!

Curtain

Act III

An hour later. At left, we can see **WALTER** *in his room, alone. He is stretched out on the bed, his shirt out and open, his arms under his head. He just lies there, looking at the ceiling.*

In the living room, **BENEATHA** *sits at the table. She is surrounded by the packing crates. She is looking off into the distance. The bell rings and* **BENEATHA** *rises to answer it. It is* **ASAGAI**, *smiling broadly. He walks into the room with energy.*

ASAGAI: I had some free time, so I came over. I thought I might help with the packing. Ah, I like the look of packing crates! A household getting ready for a journey! It makes some people sad, but for me it is another feeling. Something full of the flow of life, do you understand? Movement, progress. It makes me think of Africa.

BENEATHA: Africa!

ASAGAI: What kind of a mood is this? Have I told you how deeply you move me?

BENEATHA: He gave away the money, Asagai.

ASAGAI: Who gave away what money?

BENEATHA: My brother. The insurance money.

ASAGAI: Gave it away?

BENEATHA: He made an investment! With a man Travis wouldn't have trusted with his most worn-out marbles.

ASAGAI: And it's gone?

BENEATHA: Gone!

ASAGAI: I'm very sorry. And you, now?

BENEATHA: Me? Me? Me, I'm nothing. When I was very small, we used to go sledding in the wintertime. The only hills we had were the ice-covered stone steps of some houses down the street. We used to fill them in with snow and make them smooth. Then we'd slide down them all day. It was very dangerous, you know. Too steep. Sure enough, one day a kid named Rufus came down too fast and hit the sidewalk. We saw his face just split open right there in front of us. And I remember looking at his face, thinking that was the end of Rufus. But the ambulance came and they took him to the hospital. They fixed the broken bones and they sewed it all up. The next time I saw Rufus, he just had a little line down his face. I never got over that.

ASAGAI: What?

BENEATHA: That one person could do that for another. Fix him up, sew up the problem, make him all right again. That was the most marvelous thing in the world. I wanted to do that. I always thought that it was the best thing in the world that a human being could do. Fix up the sick, you know, make them whole again. That was truly being God . . .

ASAGAI: You wanted to be God?

BENEATHA: No, I wanted to cure. It used to be so important to me. I wanted to cure. It used to matter. I used to care. I mean about people and how their bodies hurt.

ASAGAI: And you've stopped caring?

BENEATHA: Yes, I think so.

ASAGAI: Why?

BENEATHA (*bitterly*): Because it doesn't seem deep enough, close enough to what ails mankind! It was a child's view—or an idealist's.[16]

ASAGAI: Children see things very well sometimes—and idealists even better.

BENEATHA: I know that's what you think. Because you are still where I left off. You with all your talk and dreams about Africa and independence!

ASAGAI: Yes!

BENEATHA: Well, what about all the crooks and thieves and just plain idiots who will come into power? They'll steal the same as before—only now they will be black and do it in the name of Africa. What about them?

ASAGAI: That will be the problem for another time. First we must get there.

BENEATHA: And where does it end?

ASAGAI: End? Who even spoke of an end? To life? To living?

BENEATHA: An end to misery! To stupidity! Don't you see there isn't any real progress, Asagai. There is only one large circle that we all march in, around and around. Each of us has our own little picture in front of us— our own little mirage that we think is the future.

ASAGAI: That is the mistake.

BENEATHA: What?

ASAGAI: What you just said about the circle. It isn't a circle. It is just a long line that reaches into infinity.[17] And because we cannot see the end, we also cannot see how it changes. Those who see the

---

16. **idealist**　a person who is impractical and unrealistic
17. **infinity**　unending time or space

changes—who dream, who will not give up—are called "idealists." Those who see only the circle, we call *them* the "realists."[18]

BENEATHA: Asagai, while I was sleeping in that bed in there, people went out and took the future right out of my hands! And nobody asked me! They just went out and changed my life!

ASAGAI: Was it your money?

BENEATHA: What?

ASAGAI: Was it your money he gave away?

BENEATHA: It belonged to all of us.

ASAGAI: But did you earn it? Would you have had it at all if your father had not died?

BENEATHA: No.

ASAGAI: Then isn't there something wrong where all dreams, good or bad, must depend on the death of a man? I never thought to see you like this, Alaiyo. You! Your brother made a mistake and now you give up on the human race! You talk about what good is struggle, what good is anything! Where are we all going, and why are we bothering!

BENEATHA: AND YOU CANNOT ANSWER IT!

ASAGAI (*shouting over her*): *I LIVE THE ANSWER!* In my village at home, it is the rare man who can even read a newspaper, or who ever sees a book at all. I will go home and much of what I will have to say will seem strange to the people of my village. But I will teach and work, and things will happen. Perhaps I will be

---

18. realists persons who are concerned with facts and practical matters

a great man. I mean, perhaps I will hold on to the truth and find my way always with the right course. And perhaps for it I will be butchered in my bed some night by the servants of the empire . . .

BENEATHA: *The martyr!*[19]

ASAGAI (*smiling*): Or perhaps I shall live to be a very old man, respected in my new nation.

BENEATHA: Oh, Asagai, I know all that.

ASAGAI: Good! Then stop moaning and groaning and tell me what you plan to do.

BENEATHA: Do?

ASAGAI: I have a bit of a suggestion.

BENEATHA: What?

ASAGAI: When it is over, you come home with me.

BENEATHA: Oh, Asagai, at this moment, you decide to be romantic!

ASAGAI: My dear, young creature of the New World. I do not mean across the city. I mean across the ocean. Home—to Africa.

BENEATHA: To Africa?

ASAGAI: Yes! To Nigeria. Home. I will show you our mountains and our stars. I will give you cool drinks from gourds. I'll teach you the old songs and the ways of our people. In time, we will pretend that you have only been away for a day. Say that you'll come. (*He takes her in his arms and kisses her.*)

---

19. martyr   a person who sacrifices life or something of great value for the sake of a principle

BENEATHA (*pulling away suddenly*): You're getting me all mixed up.

ASAGAI: Why?

BENEATHA: Too many things have happened today. I must sit down and think. I don't know what I feel about anything right this minute.

(*She sits down and props her chin on her fist.*)

ASAGAI (*charmed*): All right, I shall leave you. No, don't get up. Just sit awhile and think. Never be afraid to sit awhile and think.

(*He exits.* BENEATHA *sits on alone. Presently* WALTER *comes from his room and starts to look for something. She looks up.*)

BENEATHA (*sarcastically*): Did you dream of yachts on Lake Michigan, Brother? Did you see yourself on that Great Day sitting down at the Conference Table, surrounded by all the mighty bald-headed men in America? All waiting for your ideas! Waiting for you—Chairman of the Board! (WALTER *finds what he is looking for—a small piece of white paper. He puts it in his pocket and rushes out without ever having looked at her. She shouts after him.*) I look at you and I see the final triumph of stupidity in the world!

(*The door slams and she returns to just sitting again.* **Ruth** *comes quickly out of* **MAMA'S** *room.*)

RUTH: Who was that?

BENEATHA: Your husband.

RUTH: Where did he go?

BENEATHA: Who knows? Maybe he has an appointment at U.S. Steel.

RUTH (*frightened*): You didn't say nothing bad to him, did you?

BENEATHA: Bad? Say anything bad to him? No—I said he was a sweet boy and full of dreams and everything is just peachy keen!

(**MAMA** *enters from her bedroom. She is lost, trying to make some sense of what has happened. She goes to her plant, which has remained on the table. She picks it up and takes it to the windowsill and sets it outside. She stands and looks at it. Then she closes the window and turns around to her children.*)

MAMA: Well, ain't it a mess in here, though? I guess we all better stop moping around and get some work done. All this unpacking and everything we got to do. One of you all better call the moving people and tell 'em not to come.

RUTH: Tell 'em not to come?

MAMA: Of course, baby. Ain't no need in 'em coming all the way here and having to go back. They charges for that, too. Lord, ever since I was a little girl, people always said, "Lena, you aims too high all the time. You needs to slow down and see life a little more like it is. Just slow down some." Me and Big Walter just didn't never learn right.

RUTH: Lena, no! We gotta go. Bennie, tell her. Tell her we can still move. The payment ain't but 125 dollars a month. We got four grown people in this house. We can work.

MAMA (*to herself*): Just aimed too high—

RUTH (*going to* MAMA *fast*): Lena, I'll work. I'll work twenty hours a day in all the kitchens in Chicago. I'll strap my baby on my back and scrub all the floors in America—but we got to MOVE! We got to get OUT OF HERE!

(MAMA *reaches out and pats* RUTH's *hand.*)

MAMA: No, I sees things differently now. Sometimes you just got to know when to give up some things, and hold on to what you got.

(WALTER *enters from the outside.*)

MAMA: Where you been, son?

WALTER (*breathing hard*): Made a call.

MAMA: To who, son?

WALTER: To The Man. (*He heads for his room.*)

MAMA: What man, baby?

WALTER: Don't you know who The Man is, Mama?

BENEATHA (*suddenly*): Lindner!

WALTER: That's right! That's good. I told him to come right over.

BENEATHA: Why? What do you want to see him for!

WALTER: We going to do business with him.

MAMA: What you talking 'bout, son?

WALTER: Talking 'bout life, Mama. You all always telling me to see life like it is. Well, I figured it out. Mama, you know life is all divided up. Between the takers and the "tooken." Yeah, some of us always getting "tooken." (*He laughs.*) People like Willy Harris, they don't never get "tooken." And you know why the rest of us do? 'Cause we all mixed up.

RUTH: What did you call that man for, Walter Lee?

WALTER: To tell him to come on over to the show. Gonna put on a show for the man.

RUTH: You talking 'bout taking them people's money to keep us from moving in that house?

WALTER: I ain't just talking 'bout it, baby. I'm telling you that's what's going to happen.

BENEATHA: Oh, God! Where is the bottom! Where is the real bottom so he can't go any farther!

WALTER: There ain't nothing but taking in this world. He who takes most is smartest—and it don't make any difference *how*.

MAMA: You making something inside me cry, son. Some awful pain inside me.

WALTER: Don't cry, Mama. Understand. The white man is going to walk in that door and write checks for more money than we ever had. It's important to him and I'm going to help him. I'm going to put on the show, Mama.

MAMA: Son, I come from five generations of people who was slaves and sharecroppers. But ain't nobody in my family never let nobody pay 'em no money that was a way of telling us we wasn't fit to walk the Earth. We ain't never been that poor. (*looking at him*) We ain't never been that dead inside.

WALTER: What's the matter with you? I didn't make this world! It was give to me this way!

MAMA: Baby, how you going to feel on the inside?

WALTER: Fine! Going to feel fine . . . a man.

MAMA: You won't have nothing left, Walter Lee.

WALTER: I'm going to look him in the eyes and say, "Yes, Mr. Lindner, that's *your* neighborhood out there! You got the right to keep it like you want. Just write the check, and the house is yours." And I'm going to say (*his voice almost breaks*), "You people just put the money in my hand and you won't have to live next to this bunch of stinking niggers." Maybe I'll get down on my black knees . . . (*He does so.* **RUTH** *and* **BENNIE** *and* **MAMA** *watch him in frozen horror.*) "Captain, Mistuh, Bossman. Oh, yassuh boss! Just gi' ussen de money, and we's ain't gwine come out deh and dirty up yo' white folks neighborhood." (*He breaks down completely.*) And I'll feel fine! Fine! FINE! (*He gets up and goes to the bedroom.*)

BENEATHA: That is not a man. That is nothing but a toothless rat.

MAMA: Yes, death done come in this here house. (*to* **BENEATHA**) You mourning your brother?

BENEATHA: He's no brother of mine.

MAMA: What you say?

BENEATHA: I said that the individual in that room is no brother of mine.

MAMA: That's what I thought you said. You feeling like you better than he is today? (**BENEATHA** *does not answer.*) Yes? What you tell him a minute ago? That he wasn't a man? You give him up for me? You done wrote his epitaph,[20] too—like the rest of the world? Well, who give you that right?

BENEATHA: Be on my side for once! You saw what he just did, Mama! You saw him—down on his knees. Didn't you teach me to despise any man who would do what he's going to do?

MAMA: Yes, I taught you that. Me and your daddy. But I thought I taught you something else, too. I thought I taught you to love him.

BENEATHA: Love him? There is nothing left to love.

MAMA: There is *always* something left to love. And if you ain't learned that, you ain't learned nothing. Have you cried for that boy today? I don't mean for yourself and for the family 'cause we lost the money. I mean for him: what he been through and what it done to him. Child, when do you think is the time to love somebody the most? When they done good and made things easy for everybody? Well, then, you ain't through learning—because that ain't the time at all. It's when he's at his lowest and can't believe in hisself 'cause the world done whipped him so!

(**TRAVIS** *bursts into the room at the end of this speech. He leaves the door open.*)

TRAVIS: Grandmama—the moving men are downstairs! The truck just pulled up.

---

20. epitaph   the writing on a monument or gravestone in memory of someone who died

MAMA: Are they, baby? They downstairs?

(*She sighs and sits.* LINDNER *appears in the doorway. He knocks lightly, to gain attention, and comes in. All turn to look at him.*)

LINDNER: Uh—hello.

(RUTH *goes to the bedroom door and opens it. She lets it swing open freely, showing* WALTER *within. He is sitting at the far corner of the room. He looks out to* LINDNER.)

RUTH: He's here.

(WALTER *slowly gets up and comes out.*)

LINDNER (*sitting at the table*): Well, I certainly was glad to hear from you people.

RUTH: Travis, you go downstairs.

MAMA (*looking into* WALTER's *eyes*): No, Travis, you stay right here. And you make him understand what you doing, Walter Lee. You teach him good. Like Willy Harris taught you. You show where our five generations done come to. Go ahead.

WALTER: Well, Mr. Lindner. We called you because me and my family . . . well, we are very plain people. I mean, I have worked as a chauffeur most of my life. My wife and my mother do domestic work in people's kitchens. I mean, we are plain people.

LINDNER: Yes, Mr. Younger.

WALTER: And, well, my father, he was a laborer most of his life.

LINDNER (*confused*): Uh, yes, yes, I understand.

WALTER: And my father *almost beat a man to death* once because this man called him a bad name—you know what I mean.

LINDNER (*frightened*): No, no, I'm afraid I don't.

WALTER: Well, what I mean is that we come from people who had a lot of *pride*. I mean—we are very proud people. And that's my sister over there and she's going to be a doctor. And we are very proud—

LINDNER: Well, I am sure that is very nice, but—

WALTER: What I am telling you is that we called you over here to tell you that we are very proud. Travis, come here. (**TRAVIS** *goes to his father.*) This is my son, and he makes the sixth generation of our family in this country. And we have all thought about your offer. And we have decided to move into our house because my father—he earned it for us brick by brick. (**MAMA** *has her eyes closed. She is rocking back and forth as if she were in church, with her head nodding the Amen yes.*) We don't want to make no trouble for nobody or fight no causes. We will try to be good neighbors. And that's *all* we got to say about that. We don't want your money. (*He turns and walks away.*)

LINDNER (*to* **MAMA**): Then I would like to appeal to you, Mrs. Younger. You are older and wiser and understand things better, I am sure . . .

MAMA: I am afraid you don't understand. My son said we was going to move and there ain't nothing left for me to say. Good-bye.

LINDNER: Well, I sure hope you people know what you're getting into.

(*He shakes his head and exits.*)

RUTH: Well, if the moving men are here, LET'S GET OUT OF HERE!

MAMA: Ain't it the truth. Look at all this here mess. Ruth, put Travis's good jacket on him. Walter Lee, fix your tie and tuck your shirt in. (*The family seems to be trying to ignore the nobility of the past moment.*) You all start on down. Ruth, where did I put that box with my skillets in it? I want to be in charge of it myself. I'm going to make us the biggest dinner we ever ate tonight. Beneatha, what's the matter with them stockings? Pull them things up, girl.

(*The family starts to file out as two* MOVING MEN *appear. The* MEN *begin to carry out some pieces of furniture.*)

BENEATHA: Mama, Asagai asked me to marry him today and go to Africa.

MAMA: You ain't old enough to marry anybody.

BENEATHA: To Africa, Mama. Be a doctor in Africa.

MAMA: Yes, baby.

WALTER: Africa! Why he want you to go to Africa?

BENEATHA: To practice there . . .

WALTER: Girl, get them silly ideas out your head! Marry yourself a man with some money . . .

BENEATHA: What do you have to do with who I marry!

WALTER: Plenty. Now I think George Murchison—

BENEATHA: George Murchison! I wouldn't marry him if he was Adam and I was Eve![21]

---

21. Adam and Eve   according to the Bible, the first two people on Earth

(**WALTER** *and* **BENEATHA** *go out yelling at each other loudly.*
RUTH *stands at the door and turns to* **MAMA**.)

MAMA: Yeah, they something all right, my children. (*quietly,
woman to woman*) He finally come into his manhood
today, didn't he? Like a rainbow after the rain . . .

RUTH: Yes, Lena.

WALTER (*from offstage*): Y'all come on! These people
charges by the hour, you know!

MAMA (*waving* **RUTH** *out*): All right, honey, go on down.
I be down directly.

(**RUTH** *exits.* **MAMA** *stands, at last alone in the living room.
Her plant has been brought in from outside and is now on
the table. She looks around, pulls her coat tight, pats her
hat, and exits. The lights dim down. The door opens and
she comes back in, grabs her plant, and goes out for the
last time.*)

Curtain

REVIEWING YOUR READING

ACT I, SCENE 1

FINDING THE MAIN IDEA

1. What is the most important thing that you learn from this scene? (A) Travis Younger has to sleep in the living room. (B) The Youngers are expecting a check for $10,000. (C) Travis needs 50 cents for school. (D) Mama has always wanted a garden.

REMEMBERING DETAILS

2. What is Beneatha studying to be? (A) a guitar teacher (B) a nurse (C) a lawyer (D) a doctor

DRAWING CONCLUSIONS

3. Mama and Big Walter moved into the apartment two weeks after they were married. We can assume that Mama has been living there (A) about 35 years. (B) about 10 years. (C) about 20 years. (D) about 60 years.

IDENTIFYING THE MOOD

4. When Walter talks to Beneatha about her education, the mood can best be described as (A) happy. (B) playful. (C) loving. (D) tense.

CRITICAL THINKING

5. **Comprehension** Why do you think Walter suggests to Beneatha that she study to be a nurse?

6. **Application** When Travis asks for 50 cents, his father gives him his last dollar. What explanation do you think Walter might give for why he did this?

7. **Analysis** Mama is against Walter's idea of starting a business with a few partners. What reasons do you think she might have for this?

ACT I, SCENE 2

FINDING THE MAIN IDEA

1. What is the most important thing that happens in this scene?
   (A) Asagai gets back from Canada. (B) The insurance check arrives.
   (C) Travis finishes his chores. (D) Beneatha sprays for roaches.

REMEMBERING DETAILS

2. What country is Asagai's home? (A) Nigeria (B) Yoruba
   (C) Liberia (D) Canada

DRAWING CONCLUSIONS

3. When Asagai brings the Nigerian robes to Beneatha, what conclusion
   can you draw? (A) He thinks all American women should wear
   Nigerian robes. (B) He gives such gifts to many women.
   (C) He wants Beneatha to sell them. (D) He cares for Beneatha.

IDENTIFYING THE MOOD

4. When Beneatha opens the gift Asagai brings, how would you
   describe the mood between them? (A) tense (B) confused
   (C) happy (D) fearful

CRITICAL THINKING

5. **Knowledge** Why does Asagai refer to Beneatha's hair as
   "mutilated"?

6. **Application** When Mama invites Asagai to come over from time to
   time for some home-cooked meals, he is touched by her generous
   offer. Why do you think he has this reaction?

7. **Synthesis** Why does Mama say that, if not for her family, she would
   give the insurance money away?

ACT II, SCENE 1

FINDING THE MAIN IDEA

1. What is the most important thing that happens in this scene?
(A) Walter pretends to be an African warrior. (B) Beneatha shows
off her new hairdo. (C) Mama puts a down payment on a house.
(D) Travis comes home late.

REMEMBERING DETAILS

2. What kind of music does Beneatha play when she models her new
robes for Ruth? (A) Nigerian (B) jazz (C) rock and roll (D) opera

DRAWING CONCLUSIONS

3. Judging from Ruth's and George Murchison's reaction to Beneatha's
hairdo, you can assume that (A) it was a popular style in those days.
(B) it was a rare style in those days. (C) only men wore their hair like
that in those days. (D) it was a style meant for children, not adults.

IDENTIFYING THE MOOD

4. Walter's mood after Mama announces her news can best be described
as (A) proud. (B) nervous. (C) annoyed. (D) angry.

CRITICAL THINKING

5. **Synthesis** Compare and contrast George Murchison and
Joseph Asagai.

6. **Comprehension** When Mama gives her news about the house, how
do Ruth and Walter react? Why do you think they each feel the way
they do?

7. **Analysis** Why do you think Walter is so hostile to George Murchison?

ACT II, SCENE 2

FINDING THE MAIN IDEA

1. What is the most important thing that happens in this scene?
   (A) Mama gives Walter the money for his investment.
   (B) Mrs. Johnson comes to visit. (C) Beneatha tells Mama that
   George Murchison is a fool. (D) Walter's employer calls.

REMEMBERING DETAILS

2. What does Mama tell Walter to do with the money? (A) use all of it
   to invest in his business (B) put it all in the bank for Beneatha's
   education (C) make a few years' payments on the new house
   (D) put $3,000 away for Beneatha's education and use the rest for
   his business

DRAWING CONCLUSIONS

3. Why does Beneatha think George Murchison is a fool? (A) because he
   is so rich (B) because he thinks she's pretty (C) because he doesn't
   value education (D) because he doesn't appreciate Nigerian music

IDENTIFYING THE MOOD

4. How would you describe Walter's mood when he's telling Travis what
   the future will be like? (A) unsure (B) hopeful (C) funny (D) worried

CRITICAL THINKING

5. **Application** Mama tells Beneatha that she'd better not waste her
   time on fools. What does this tell you about Mama's values?

6. **Comprehension** Beneatha says, "Mama, if there are two things we,
   as a people, have got to overcome, one is the Ku Klux Klan—and the
   other is Mrs. Johnson." What does she mean by this?

7. **Synthesis** What makes Mama decide to give Walter the rest of
   the money?

ACT II, SCENE 3

FINDING THE MAIN IDEA

1. What is the most important news that the family finds out about in this scene? (A) The new curtains might not fit the windows. (B) Karl Lindner represents the Clybourne Park Improvement Association. (C) Bobo waited many hours for Willy. (D) Willy stole the rest of the insurance money.

REMEMBERING DETAILS

2. What did Mr. Lindner offer the Youngers? (A) a check for more than they paid for the house (B) a letter welcoming them to the neighborhood (C) the rules of the Clybourne Park community (D) an invitation to a neighborhood get-together

DRAWING CONCLUSIONS

3. When Ruth offers Mr. Lindner another chair, saying he doesn't look comfortable, we can assume that (A) the chair he is using is too worn out to be comfortable. (B) he is nervous about what he has come to say. (C) it is too hot in the apartment. (D) it is too cold in the apartment.

IDENTIFYING THE MOOD

4. When Mama finds out what happened to the money, her mood can best be described as (A) disappointed. (B) indifferent. (C) enraged. (D) relieved.

CRITICAL THINKING

5. **Knowledge** What kind of person would you say Mr. Lindner is? Use evidence from the play to support your answer.

6. **Synthesis** What explanation might Mama give for the attachment she feels toward her little plant?

7. **Application** Walter adds Beneatha's education money to the money for buying his own business. How do you think he might justify this?

ACT III

FINDING THE MAIN IDEA

1. What is the most important thing that happens in this act?
(A) The Youngers decide to move after all. (B) Asagai comes over to
help pack. (C) Asagai asks Beneatha to move to Africa with him.
(D) Mr. Lindner comes over again.

REMEMBERING DETAILS

2. What made Beneatha want to be a doctor? (A) She spent time in a
hospital once. (B) Her friend Rufus wanted to be a doctor. (C) She
saw what doctors did to help a badly injured child. (D) She wanted
to go to Africa and cure people.

DRAWING CONCLUSIONS

3. Based on what you know about Beneatha, what will she probably
do in the future? (A) marry George Murchison (B) become an
accomplished guitar player (C) decide to become a nurse
(D) become a doctor and move to Nigeria with Asagai

IDENTIFYING THE MOOD

4. After Walter's speech to Mr. Lindner, how would you describe
Mama's mood? (A) jittery (B) proud (C) sad (D) protective

CRITICAL THINKING

5. **Synthesis** Based on what Walter says to Mr. Lindner, how would
you say his attitude has changed since the beginning of the play?

6. **Application** Mama remembers people telling her that she was
always aiming too high. If you were in Mama's place, what would
you say to them?

7. **Application** If you could talk to the members of the Clybourne Park
Improvement Association, what would you say?